PROJECTS FOR RADIO AMATEURS
AND S.W.L.s

by

R. A. PENFOLD

**BERNARD BABANI (publishing) LTD
THE GRAMPIANS
SHEPHERDS BUSH ROAD
LONDON W6 7NF
ENGLAND**

Please Note

Although every care has been taken with the production of this book to ensure that any projects, designs, modifications and/or programs etc. contained herewith, operate in a correct and safe manner and also that any components specified are normally available in Great Britain, the Publishers do not accept responsibility in any way for the failure, including fault in design, of any project, design, modification or program to work correctly or to cause damage to any other equipment that it may be connected to or used in conjunction with, or in respect of any other damage or injury that may be so caused, nor do the Publishers accept responsibility in any way for the failure to obtain specified components.

Notice is also given that if equipment that is still under warranty is modified in any way or used or connected with home-built equipment then that warranty may be void.

© 1992 BERNARD BABANI (publishing) LTD

First Published — April 1992

British Library Cataloguing in Publication Data
Penfold, R. A.
    Projects for Radio Amateurs and SWLs
    I. Title
    621.3841

    ISBN 0 85934 249 2

Printed and bound in Great Britain by Cox & Wyman Ltd, Reading

Preface

Traditionally, short wave radio equipment is largely or totally home constructed. This tradition seems to have waned somewhat over the past ten to twenty years though, and I suppose that many radio shacks are now totally devoid of home constructed equipment. However, commercial "black boxes" are not totally dominant, and in recent times there has been some revival in the construction of radio equipment. Even those who are not at all interested in building receivers and transmitters are often keen to experiment with home built aerials, and to construct some accessories for their ready-made equipment.

This book provides a number of circuits for the short wave enthusiast. These are mainly gadgets to aid short wave reception, so they are mostly suitable for both licensed radio amateurs and short wave listeners. The circuits include such things as an aerial tuning unit, audio filters (including notch and a high performance bandpass type), and a volume expander.

Where appropriate there are details of how to set up and use the equipment, plus notes on any unusual aspects of construction. No precise constructional details are provided though, and it is assumed that the reader has some experience at electronic project construction. On the other hand, some of the projects are very simple, and should be within the capabilities of practically anyone who has previously built one or two simple projects. Having built some of the more simple projects, there should be little difficulty in progressing to the more complex circuits.

R. A. Penfold

Contents

Chapter 1

R.F./I.F. PROJECTS

Some of the projects in this chapter are simply added between the aerial and the antenna socket of the receiver. These are relatively safe, and there is little risk of damaging the receiver if a mistake should be made. A few of these projects require internal connection to the receiver, and these have to be regarded as more risky. Bear in mind that modifying equipment that is fairly new can result in guarantees being invalidated. Unless you really know what you are doing there is a very real risk of doing expensive damage to a receiver when attempting modifications. With modern short wave equipment it is even possible to render devices totally inoperative simply by getting some of the circuits misaligned. This can involve a costly return to the service department of your supplier, so that the set can be realigned with the aid of some advanced test equipment and a trained engineer. Unless you really know what you are doing, you might even end up trying to add a circuit to a receiver which is totally incompatible with the add-on circuit!

Unless you have the necessary expertise, it is definitely a good idea to restrict yourself to the projects which can be built as external and separate units, and which require no modification whatever to the receiver. Where there is a choice of building a project as an external unit or an internal add-on, it is definitely advisable for those of limited experience to opt for building the project as a self-contained external unit. Projects which do involve internal connections to the receiver can be left until the requisite expertise has been gained.

Crystal Calibrator

Many modern short wave receivers use crystal controlled frequency synthesis techniques, together with digital read-outs. Others use v.c.o.s, but have a digital frequency readout provided by what is basically a built-in d.f.m. circuit. Either way, you generally know the reception frequency to the nearest kHz or so, or in some cases the readout is accurate to

1

within a few Hz. With older and many home constructed short wave receivers the accuracy of the frequency readout is often far less good. Some older sets do actually have quite good mechanical frequency readouts. These are accurate enough for most purposes provided the set is maintained in good alignment. With many sets though, the resolution of the frequency readout is so coarse, particularly on the higher frequency bands, that frequencies can not be read reliably. I have had receivers where you would be doing well to get within 100kHz of the desired frequency on the highest frequency bands.

A crystal calibrator is a useful device if you have a receiver with a mechanical frequency readout. If the set is one with a good quality readout, a crystal calibrator can be used to check the calibration. It can also be used to aid realignment if this should prove necessary from time to time. However, bear in mind the warning given previously about the possible consequences of inexperienced twiddling around inside complex communications receivers. For a receiver which has an inadequate frequency readout, a calibrator enables the set to be accurately tuned to a particular frequency.

Basically all a crystal calibrator does is to provide an output at a certain frequency, and with very good frequency accuracy. Most devices of this type actually provide several output frequencies. Figure 1.1 shows the circuit diagram for a simple calibrator that provides six output frequencies from 10kHz to 4MHz. It might seem to be rather useless to have such a limited range of frequencies, including one that is so low that it is within the audio range. However, calibrators are designed to have output signals that are rich in harmonics. A 1MHz output for example, will also provide outputs at 2MHz, 3MHz, 4MHz, 5MHz, etc., to beyond the 30MHz upper limit of the short wave range. In this way a calibrator can actually provide any output frequency you are ever likely to need.

On the face of it you only need one fundamental output frequency at a fairly low output frequency. For example, an output at 10kHz will provide calibration signals at 10kHz intervals throughout the short wave bands. In a practical situation this sort of thing is not much use on its own. You could only tell which calibration frequency was which if your

2

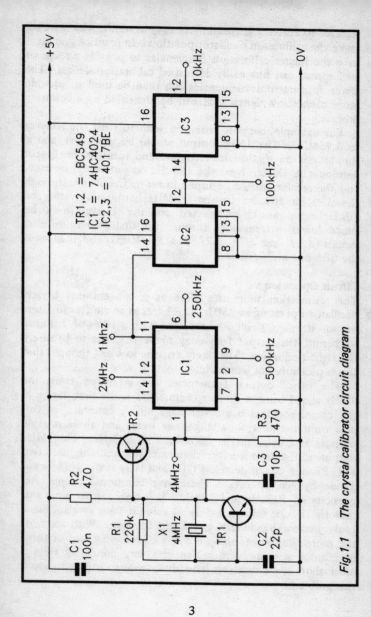

Fig. 1.1   The crystal calibrator circuit diagram

3

receiver had a very accurate frequency readout, which would make the calibration oscillator pointless! In practice you must have the higher calibration frequencies to provide a range of well spread out but easily identified calibration signals. The lower fundamental frequencies can then be used to provide more calibration signals that can be identified by a counting process.

For example, suppose that you wish to tune the receiver to 3.75MHz. The 1MHz output would be used first, and it should not be too difficult to find and identify the fourth harmonic at 4MHz. Next the 100kHz output would be used, and the receiver would be tuned lower in frequency, through the 3.9MHz and on to the 3.8MHz harmonic. Next the 10kHz signal would be selected, and the receiver would be tuned lower in frequency, through the first four calibration signals (3.79, and 3.78, 3.77, and 3.76MHz), and then onto the fifth one at 3.75MHz.

Circuit Operation

This calibration unit uses TR1 as a conventional crystal oscillator operating at 4MHz. TR2 acts as an emitter follower output stage. C2 could be replaced with a 10/60pF trimmer to permit the output frequency to be trimmed to precisely the right frequency. The likely error is so small though, that this is probably not worthwhile.

The other output frequencies are produced from the 4MHz signal using a divider chain. IC1 is the first device in the chain, and this is a seven stage binary counter. In this case only the first four stages are used, and these provide outputs at 2MHz, 1MHz, 500kHz, and 250kHz. The 1MHz output is fed to a further divider chain, and this uses two 4017BE one of ten decoders (IC2 and IC3) as straightforward divide by ten circuits. These give additional output frequencies of 100kHz and 10kHz. It is only fair to point out that the 10kHz output is only of value if your receiver has a fairly narrow bandwidth and sharp filtering. With some of the more simple sets there is a risk of receiving two or three harmonics at once, which can give very confusing results. Most short wave receivers have sharp enough tuning to avoid this problem.

With units of this type the outputs are often taken to separate output sockets. However, if preferred a six way (break before make) rotary switch can be used to provide switching between the six outputs and a single output socket. A three way switch could be used to switch the input of IC2 (pin 14) between the 1MHz, 500kHz, and 250kHz outputs of IC1. This would permit additional output frequencies of 50kHz, 25kHz, 5kHz, and 2.5kHz to be obtained. The lowest two frequencies would probably only be of use with receivers that have very sharp i.f. filtering.

The current consumption of the circuit is approximately 12 milliamps. The circuit is designed for operation on a conventional (for logic circuits) 5 volt supply, but it will work quite well from a 4.5 volt battery supply if preferred. Construction of the unit should be quite straightforward, but note that all three integrated circuits are CMOS types. They therefore require the standard anti-static handling precautions.

Note that the outputs should not be direct coupled to the aerial input of the receiver. This would provide an excessive coupling, and would probably place a virtual short circuit on the output of the calibrator! A very loose coupling normally gives best results. Simply connect a very short piece of insulated wire to the aerial socket of the receiver, and another short insulated wire to the appropriate output of the calibrator. An adequate coupling should be obtained with the two wires placed close together, but they can be twisted together if a stronger coupling is needed.

In general, the higher the harmonic, the weaker the output signal. The 3MHz harmonic of the 1MHz fundamental signal will therefore be much stronger than (say) the 15MHz harmonic of the 100kHz signal. Another point to bear in mind is that even harmonics (twice the fundamental, four times the fundamental, etc.) tend to be much weaker than the odd harmonics. In theory, with a squarewave output signal the even harmonics should be totally absent. In practice there are usually imperfections in the output signal that prevent this from happening. Some harmonics, particularly the even ones, may be relatively weak though, and it pays to be on the look-out just in case there is the occasional missing harmonic.

Components for Crystal Calibrator (Fig.1.1)

Resistors (All 0.25 watt 5% carbon film)
R1   220k
R2   470R
R3   470R

Capacitors
C1   100n ceramic
C2   22p polystyrene
C3   10p polystyrene

Semiconductors
TR1   BC549
TR2   BC549
IC1   74HC4024
IC2   4017BE
IC3   4017BE

Miscellaneous
X1   4MHz wire-ended crystal
            2mm socket (6 off)
            14 pin d.i.l. i.c. holder
            16 pin d.i.l. i.c. holder (2 off)
            Circuit board, case, wire, solder, etc.

Aerial Tuning Unit

An aerial tuning unit, or just "a.t.u." as this device is probably better known, is a passive device which can be used with a transmitter or a receiver to provide a better impedance match between the aerial and the receiver/transmitter. These days a.t.u.s are mainly used with receivers that are operated with so-called long-wire antennas. Transmitters that are suitable for use with long-wire aerials usually come equipped with some form of antenna matching circuit. Anyway, the a.t.u. design described here should work properly with a suitable transmitter provided the components used have adequate ratings for the voltages and currents involved.

The literature on a.t.u.s often talks in terms of these units providing gain, but this is not a strictly accurate way of looking at things. Being passive devices they can not provide any power gain. However, they can increase signal strengths by providing a better signal transfer from the aerial to the input of the receiver. Although it may seem to be a little strange to think in terms of a piece of wire having a source impedance, a simple wire aerial, like any signal source, must have an output impedance. By acting as an impedance transformer, an a.t.u. can provide a good match between practically any length of wire and any receiver. This gives an effective boost in signal strengths that is between 0dB if there is already a good impedance match, and about 10 to 12dB if there is a very poor impedance match without the a.t.u. Typically signal strengths are increased by about 6dB.

There is another advantage in adding an a.t.u. which is that it provides an extra tuned circuit in the r.f. circuitry of the receiver. This helps to reduce spurious responses such as i.f. breakthrough and the image response. The degree to which an a.t.u. will help to attenuate spurious responses is perhaps something that has tended to be slightly exaggerated in the past. Bear in mind the a.t.u. is only providing one additional tuned circuit, and what is not likely to be a particularly high Q tuned circuit at that. It will usually provide a worthwhile reduction in spurious responses, but it can not reasonably be expected to completely eliminate the problem when used with a receiver that suffers badly from one or more forms of breakthrough.

Circuit Operation

Figure 1.2 shows the circuit diagram for an a.t.u. of conventional design. At first sight this circuit tends to look as though it will not do a great deal, but it basically consists of a parallel tuned circuit having L1 as the inductive element and the series capacitance of VC1/2 as the capacitive element. Conventionally a single-wound transformer used to provide impedance matching would be along the lines of Figure 1.3(a). L1 and C1 form a parallel tuned circuit giving a high input impedance. A signal at a lower impedance is available from the tapping on L1. A low to high impedance transfer can be obtained if the input and output are simply swapped over.

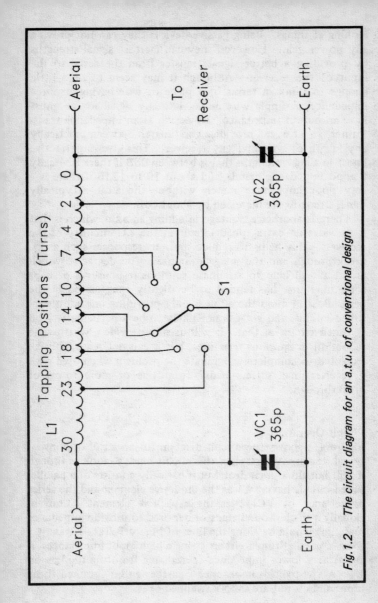

Fig.1.2   The circuit diagram for an a.t.u. of conventional design

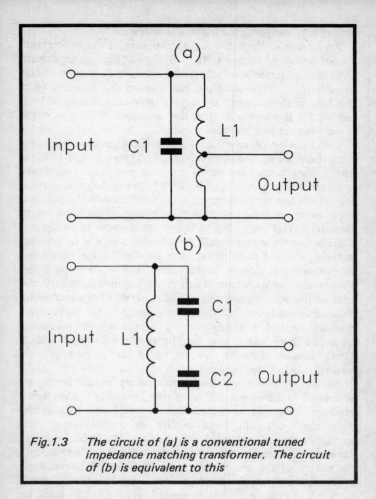

Fig. 1.3   The circuit of (a) is a conventional tuned
            impedance matching transformer. The circuit
            of (b) is equivalent to this

The circuit of Figure 1.3(b) is equivalent to that of Figure
1.3(a). The parallel tuned circuit is formed by L1 and the
series capacitance of C1 and C2. Again there is a high input
impedance and a low output impedance from the capacitive
tapping on the tuned circuit formed at the junction of C1 and
C2. Also as before, a low to high impedance match can be

obtained by swapping the input and output.

An a.t.u is really just a slight reworking of the basic transformer circuit of Figure 1.3(b). By having the two capacitors variable it is possible to adjust the resonant frequency of the tuned circuit. The multiple tappings on the inductor (L1) also help in this respect. By varying the relative values of VC1 and VC2 it is possible to shift the capacitive tapping in order to produce the best impedance match.

Construction of an a.t.u. is not difficult in most respects, since there are so few components. It is just a matter of hardwiring everything, keeping all the wiring as short and direct as reasonably possible. The only difficulty is the multi-tapped coil which has to be home-made. Traditionally the coil is a large air-cored type on a former about 25 millimetres in diameter. You may have to improvise in order to produce a suitable former which should be made of a plastic or ceramic material, and not from metal. Use about 20 s.w.g. enamelled copper wire and closely spaced turns. Throw up loops in the wire at the points where tappings are required, and tape the ends of the winding securely in place. Try to keep everything reasonably neat with all the turns running in the same direction and wound in a single layer. Scrape off the insulation from the wire loops and tin them with plenty of solder. There should then be no difficulty in making reliable connections to these tappings.

S1 can be a 12 way single pole rotary switch having its adjustable end-stop set for seven way operation. Although a value of 365p has been specified for VC1 and VC2 in the components list, any good quality air spaced components having a value of around 350p to 500p should be perfectly suitable. It is not necessary to use a coaxial cable to couple the output of the tuning unit to the receiver. Whatever type of connecting cable is used it should be reasonably short.

A lot of trial and error is needed when initially using an a.t.u. S1 must be tried at various settings with VC1 and VC2 being repeatedly adjusted in order to optimise signal strengths at each setting. This will eventually reveal the optimum set of adjustments for that band, but these will only be the optimum settings for that particular band. You must repeat the procedure in order to determine the best settings for each

10

band that you use. Looking on the bright side, once a set of optimum settings have been located, these can be marked around the control knobs of S1, VC1, and VC2 so that the unit can be quickly set up for operation on any band. Of course, any changes to the aerial will make it necessary to find a new group of adjustments for each band.

In theory an a.t.u. will work with any long-wire aerial, but in practice it is not likely to be of much use when used with short indoor aerials, whip aerials, etc. Some receivers have a high impedance aerial input for use with short aerials, and an input such as this is likely to give better results than using a low impedance input plus an a.t.u. If your receiver lacks such an input, refer to the section of this chapter which describes a simple active aerial.

Components for Aerial Tuning Unit (Fig.1.2)

Capacitors
VC1   365p air spaced
VC2   365p air spaced

Inductors
L1   see text and below

Miscellaneous
S1   12 way 1 pole rotary with adjustable end-stop
                       3 control knobs
                       20 s.w.g. enamelled copper wire for L1
                       approximately 20mm diameter former for L1
                       case, input and output sockets, connecting
                       cable, hook-up wire, solder, etc.

Wave Trap
The usual approach to dealing with spurious responses is to add tuned circuits in the r.f. circuitry of the receiver to narrow the r.f. response. This leaves the sensitivity of the set on its main response largely unaffected, but reduces the gain on all spurious responses. The drawback of this system is that it does not always give very much attenuation of the particular response which is producing troublesome interference.

As an example of this, many short wave sets which have a first intermediate frequency of about 455kHz do not provide very good image rejection on the high frequency bands. This can often give problems on the 14MHz amateur band where strong breakthrough of broadcast stations on the nearby 19 metre band tends to occur. Adding extra r.f. tuned circuits will reduce the image response, but normal tuned circuits at 14MHz or so have quite wide bandwidths. The attenuation could well be no more than about 12dB per tuned circuit, which would still leave significant breakthrough of strong broadcast signals.

An alternative approach is to add a wave trap in the aerial lead. A wave trap is merely a parallel tuned circuit added in series with the aerial, as shown in Figure 1.4. At and close to

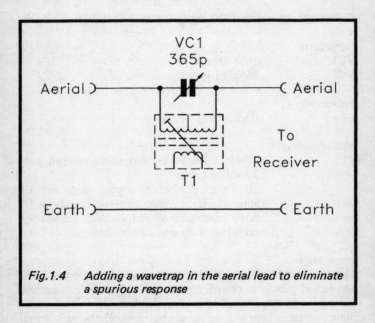

Fig.1.4 *Adding a wavetrap in the aerial lead to eliminate a spurious response*

its resonant frequency a parallel tuned circuit has a very high impedance. At other frequencies its impedance is quite low. By adjusting the tuned circuit to resonate at the same frequency as an interfering signal, that signal can be completely eliminated.

This method is not without drawbacks. The most obvious of these is that the circuit only combats one spurious response, but this is not a major shortcoming as it is quite likely that there will only be one spurious response that is causing significant problems. The wave trap will provide some attenuation at the main reception frequency, but in my experience the loss of sensitivity has never been significant. All in all, a wave trap usually represents the most simple and effective method of combatting spurious responses.

VC1 could be a trimmer capacitor rather than a variable type, but using a variable capacitor has the advantage that the unit can be adjusted to completely null any signal on the spurious response. Bear in mind that setting the unit for maximum attenuation of the spurious response with the receiver tuned to the middle of the band may well give inadequate attenuation when the receiver is tuned towards either end of the band. When the receiver's tuning is adjusted, the frequency of the spurious response usually moves in sympathy with the shifts in the main tuning.

T1 can be any ready-made aerial or r.f. coil intended for the frequency range in which the spurious response lies. Remember that the tuned circuit must operate at the frequency of the spurious response, and not at the reception frequency. If you do not know the approximate frequency range of the breakthrough it will probably be necessary to resort to some trial and error. If you have some of the old Denco coils these are well suited to this application. So are the Toko aerial and r.f. coils. In both cases there will be a coupling winding and (or) a tapping on the main winding. Any tappings or coupling windings should just be ignored. It is only the main winding, and all of it, that are required in this application.

It is not essential to use a proper aerial or r.f. transformer in this application. A simple r.f. choke seems to provide quite good results. A value of $33\mu H$ provides coverage of the low frequency bands, $2.2\mu H$ gives coverage of the middle frequency bands, and $0.5\mu H$ is suitable for the high frequency bands. Another alternative is to wind your own coil. Using a dust iron cored coil former of about 9.5 millimetres in diameter,

43, 16, and 6 turns will provide coverage of the low, medium, and high frequency bands respectively.

If i.f. breakthrough should be a problem, then replace VC1 and T1 with the tuned winding of an i.f. transformer. The core of the i.f. transformer is adjusted to minimise the breakthrough.

The cable which connects the output of the unit to the receiver should either be a screened type or it should be very short. Otherwise there is a risk that pickup in this cable will effectively reduce the attenuation provided by the wave trap.

Add-on B.F.O.

There are numerous short wave receivers which are intended mainly for short wave broadcast reception, but which also cover one or more of the short wave amateur bands. In particular, the 40 metre band is within the coverage of many portable short wave sets due to its close proximity to the 41 metre broadcast band. While most sets of this type are not much use for serious DXing on the amateur bands, they are useful for casual amateur bands listening, and their portability means that you can use them practically anywhere.

A problem with many of these portable short wave receivers is that they lack a b.f.o. This renders them unsuitable for short wave amateur bands use where the main modes of operation are c.w. and s.s.b. Ordinary a.m. is conspicuous by its absence on these bands. In most cases it is possible to overcome this shortcoming by using an add-on b.f.o. Ideally this would be built into the set and powered from its battery supply. This may not always be feasible as there can be very little spare space inside these receivers, or you may simply be unwilling to make modifications to the receiver. An external b.f.o. with its own battery supply will then do the job just as well, but will obviously be a little less convenient in use.

Figure 1.5 shows the circuit diagram for a simple add-on b.f.o. circuit. It has to be pointed out that this circuit is designed to operate at frequencies of around 455kHz to 470 kHz. Accordingly, it will only work with receivers that have an intermediate frequency that lies within this range. In practice virtually all portable short wave receivers have an intermediate frequency in this range, but before building the

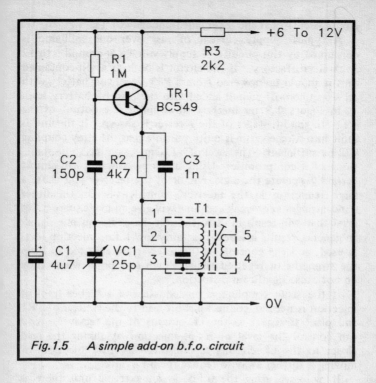

Fig.1.5   A simple add-on b.f.o. circuit

unit it would be advisable to check the intermediate frequency by referring to the receiver's instruction booklet. These usually include a technical specification page that includes this kind of information.

Circuit Operation

The circuit has TR1 operating in the emitter follower mode. This type of amplifier has its input and output in-phase, but provides slightly less than unity voltage gain. The output of the amplifier is coupled into part of T1's tuned winding. This gives a stepped-up voltage across the full winding, and C2 couples the amplified signal into the base of TR1. The voltage step-up through T1 provides more than unity voltage gain in the feedback path, and as this feedback is positive, the

15

circuit oscillates at the reasonant frequency of T1.

A typical supply current of just over one milliamp is consumed by this circuit. A supply voltage of around 6 to 12 volts is satisfactory. If the circuit is built as a self-contained unit it should be powered from a PP3 size 9 volt battery with an s.p.s.t. on/off switch added into the positive battery lead.

In Figure 1.5 no method of coupling the output of the b.f.o. to the i.f. stages of the receiver is shown. If the unit is built into a receiver it is quite possible that the stray coupling will be sufficient. The level of b.f.o. injection has to be something of a compromise. Using a strong coupling will almost certainly operate the a.g.c. circuit of the receiver and cause a large reduction in the receiver's sensitivity. On the other hand, using a very weak coupling will give an inadequate b.f.o. level that will result in distortion on the audio output signal. In general, results are best if a fairly low b.f.o. injection level is used, and the controls of the receiver are adjusted to keep the strengths of received signals down to a point where they do not cause significant distortion.

If the stray coupling is inadequate and a higher level of injection is needed, connect a short lead to the emitter of TR1 and place this near to the i.f. circuits of the receiver. You can control the level of b.f.o. injection by taking the lead closer to the i.f. circuits to boost the level of injection, or moving it further away to reduce the b.f.o. level.

If you are using the b.f.o. as an external unit there is little chance of stray coupling providing enough b.f.o. injection. Connecting a short lead to the emitter of TR1 and placing it alongside the receiver should provide a high enough injection level. The b.f.o. level can again be controlled by taking the lead closer to the receiver or moving it further away.

The core of T1 is adjusted so that the output frequency of the unit is at the middle of the receiver's passband with VC1 at half maximum capacitance. The easiest way to do this is to first tune the receiver accurately to an a.m. station. With VC1 at a mid setting, the core of T1 is adjusted to produce a heterodyne tone as the carrier wave of the a.m. station and the b.f.o. signal interact. Carefully adjust the core of T1 for the lowest audio tone that can be obtained.

In use VC1 should be offset slightly from its central setting when listening to s.s.b. stations. In theory it should be tuned higher in frequency for lower sideband reception, and lower in frequency for upper sideband signals. Due to the way in which superhet receivers operate, the frequencies in the i.f. stages can be (and often are) inverted. This effectively converts an upper sideband signal to a lower sideband type, and vice versa. It is therefore advisable to try offsets in both directions to determine which one gives the best results in practice. Note that lower sideband is dominant on the low frequency bands, while it is mainly upper sideband that is used on the high frequency bands.

Tuning in s.s.b. stations is much more difficult than tuning to ordinary a.m. broadcasts. The tuning must be within about 30Hz of the correct frequency in order to produce an audio output of acceptable pitch. Portable receivers which lack a b.f.o. might prove to be very difficult to tune accurately to s.s.b. transmissions. This is not really a design fault in these receivers, which in fairness were simply not designed for this type of reception. Anyway, the easiest solution to the problem is to tune to stations as accurately as possible using the tuning control, and to then use the b.f.o. frequency control (VC1) to effectively fine-tune the signal.

Components for Simple Add-on B.F.O. (Fig.1.5)

Resistors (all 0.25 watt 5% carbon film)
R1   1M
R2   4k7
R3   2k2

Capacitors
C1   4μ7 63V elect
C2   150p ceramic plate
C3   1n polyester
VC1   25p air spaced (Jackson C804)

Semiconductor
TR1   BC549

T1   Toko YHCS11100AC
               Circuit board, control knob, wire, solder,
               etc.

Note that for a self-contained unit a PP3 size battery, matching battery connector, s.p.s.t. on/off switch, and a small case will also be required.

Simple Active Aerial

As pointed out previously, some short wave receivers offer two aerial inputs for simple single wire antennas. One is a low impedance input for an ordinary long wire aerial, and the other is a high impedance input for a shorter aerial. This shorter aerial could be something as basic as a telescopic or whip aerial, or it could be an indoor wire aerial of some kind. In either case results tend to be disappointing if such an aerial is used with an ordinary low impedance aerial input.

If a receiver lacks a high impedance aerial socket, but circumstances are such that a long wire aerial can not be accommodated, it is often possible to obtain improved results using a simple active antenna circuit. There is actually an extremely simple alternative if you are prepared to delve into the front-end circuit of your receiver. The aerial normally couples to a low impedance coupling winding on an r.f. transformer, as in Figure 1.6. With a bipolar transistor front-end the output from the r.f. transformer is usually taken via a low impedance secondary winding, or a tapping on the tuned winding. With f.e.t and valve based circuits the tuned circuit normally couples straight into the gate or grid of the amplifying device in the r.f. amplifier.

An easy way to obtain improved results with a relatively short aerial is to loosely couple the aerial into the tuned circuit via a low value capacitor, as in Figure 1.7. This gives a high impedance coupling which provides a better signal transfer with short aerials. The value of 10p for the coupling capacitor is a suggested starting point, and it is advisable to experiment with a few values to determine which one gives the best results with your particular setup. Too low a value gives an inadequate coupling, while an excessively high value

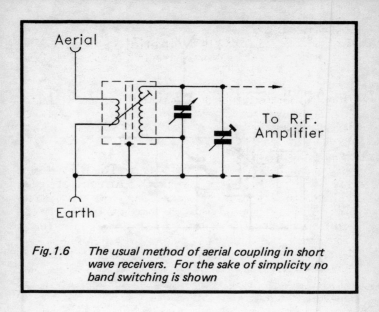

Fig. 1.6   The usual method of aerial coupling in short wave receivers. For the sake of simplicity no band switching is shown

will produce loading and detuning effects on the tuned circuit. This generally manifests itself in the form of strong signals breaking through to the output. You might prefer to use a trimmer capacitor of around 5/30p in value, and this can then be tried at various settings to find the best compromise. With a very short aerial such as a telescopic type results might be best with the aerial connected direct to the tuned circuit.

The simple active alternative is to use an amplifier ahead of the receiver's aerial input. This amplifier can provide a certain amount of voltage gain, or it can simply be a buffer stage to provide a high to low impedance transformation. In most cases there is no point in using any voltage gain, since the increased noise level this produces prevents any real improvement in performance. Weak signals are boosted, but the noise level is boosted by the same amount. This gives boosted signals that are still inaudible above the higher noise level.

Figure 1.8 shows the circuit diagram for a simple buffer amplifier which is suitable for use in a simple active antenna

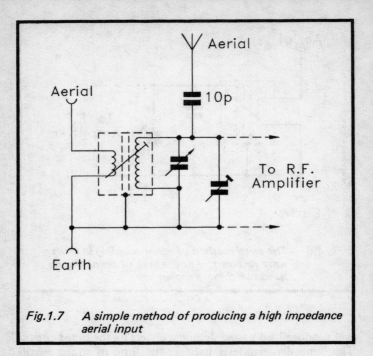

Fig.1.7   A simple method of producing a high impedance aerial input

application.   This is just an emitter follower buffer stage having biasing provided by R1 and R2, R3 as the emitter load, and C1 to provide d.c. blocking at the output. The aerial is direct coupled to the input. In theory it could be advantageous to use a low value coupling capacitor at the input. This would reduce any stray pickup of low frequency noise which would reduce the large signal handling performance of TR1. In practice I have never found this to be particularly worthwhile.

A better way of improving the large signal handling performance of the circuit is to use an 18 volt power supply (i.e. two 9 volt batteries wired in series). The current consumption from a 9 volt supply is about 6 to 7 milliamps, but it is around 14 to 15 milliamps when using an 18 volt supply. When using a single battery a PP3 size is just about adequate, but when using two batteries in series a higher capacity type would be

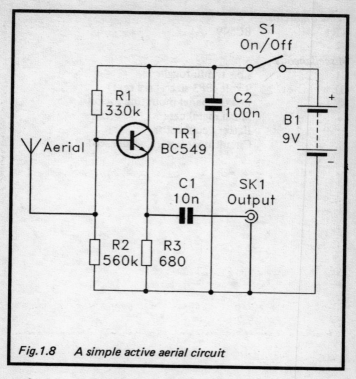

Fig.1.8   A simple active aerial circuit

preferable. Two PP9 batteries should have a long operating life. The coupling cable to the receiver does not have to be a screened type, but it is advisable to use a reasonably short cable here (i.e. one about 0.5 to 1 metre long).

Components for Simple Active Aerial (Fig.1.8)

Resistors (all 0.25 watt 5% carbon film)
R1   330k
R2   560k
R3   680R

Capacitors
C1   10n polyester
C2   100n ceramic

21

Semiconductor
TR1   BC549

Miscellaneous
S1   s.p.s.t. min toggle
B1   9 volt (PP3 size — see text)
SK1   Coaxial panel mounting socket
                  Small metal case
                  Battery connector
                  Circuit board, wire, solder, etc.

Chapter 2

AUDIO FREQUENCY PROJECTS

Radio communications is not only about the processing of radio frequency signals. The signal starts off as an audio type at the transmitter, and is converted back to an audio type at the receiver. Processing of the audio signal can have a significant effect on results. It is probably at the receiving end of a system that audio processing is of most value, but it can also be used to good effect at the transmitting end.

Audio processors are an attractive proposition for the home constructor since there is normally no problem in building them as self-contained external units. They are simply fed from a "tape" or "phones" socket in the case of receiver add-ons, or added ahead of the microphone input in the case of transmitter add-ons. This avoids the need for even the most simple of modifications to the main equipment. There can sometimes be an advantage in adding an audio processor into the main equipment, or in making a slight modification to the main unit, but this is not usually essential.

Bandpass Filter

For speech communications only a relatively narrow band-width is required. There seems to be something less than total agreement on the acceptable frequency limits for carrying intelligible speech. Traditionally it is held that the pass-band should be from around 300Hz to about 3kHz at the very least. Recent research seems to suggest that a significantly narrower bandwidth can be used successfully. Most modern communications equipment probably uses a bandwidth somewhat narrower than the traditional 300Hz to 3kHz, but in most cases only marginally narrower.

There is a problem with many older receivers, and the less expensive modern types, in that they provide intermediate frequency filtering that is far from optimum. Some receivers, especially the older types, lack any form of crystal or mechanical filtering, and rely on a number of conventional L — C tuned circuits to provide the filtering. This usually gives a passband that is about right for ordinary a.m. reception, but is far too wide for s.s.b. signals. Probably more than twice as wide as is really necessary in fact. Also, the attenuation rate in the "skirts" of the passband is not very high with such an arrangement.

Inexpensive modern receivers often have some mechanical or ceramic filtering to aid the filtering provided by the intermediate frequency transformers, but these filters are usually inexpensive types which are intended for use in ordinary broadcast receivers. These provide some improvement over i.f. circuits which rely solely on i.f. transformers for their selectivity. However, they rarely provide a narrow enough bandwidth, and the attenuation rates do not compare with those provided by high quality crystal and ceramic filters.

An audio filter can be very beneficial when added to a receiver that has an excessive bandwidth for s.s.b. reception. It would be an exaggeration to claim that an audio filter can make a receiver which has mediocre or poor i.f. filtering as good as one fitted with a top notch crystal or ceramic filter. The attenuation rate of an audio filter is likely to be much lower than that of a high quality i.f. filter. There can also be problems with strong signals that are outside the audio passband, but which are within the i.f. passband. The main one is that such a signal will operate the automatic gain control (a.g.c.) circuit of the receiver, and this will reduce the volume from the wanted signal.

Despite these limitations an audio filter can substantially improve results when used with a set that has an excessive i.f. bandwidth. The short wave bands tend to be so crowded these days that adjacent channel interference is a major problem. An audio filter will be of most use for s.s.b. reception on overcrowded amateur bands where there is a severe problem with "monkey chatter" etc. It is only fair to point out that an audio filter is unlikely to make a significant improvement when used with a receiver that has top quality i.f. filtering. Also, the improvement is likely to be relatively small during ordinary a.m. reception on the broadcast bands.

Circuit Operation

There are a number of possible approaches to audio band-pass filtering, and here we will consider two of them. The first is based on inexpensive and readily available components, but gives a less marked improvement in results. The second approach relies on the use of quite large inductors which are relatively expensive and difficult to obtain. It provides substantially better results though.

C − R filtering offers the least expensive method of providing audio filtering. Conventional C − R bandpass filters provide bandwidths that are far too narrow to be of any use in the current context. Better results seem to be obtained using what are really separate highpass and lowpass filters which provide a bandpass action when used together. In fact it is not essential to use both, and you might prefer to use just the lowpass filter to combat the high frequency "monkey chatter" that is usually the main source of QRM on the amateur bands.

In my opinion at any rate, it is well worthwhile including the highpass filtering as there is almost invariably a lot more low frequency interference than you would think. Due to the way the human hearing mechanism works, you tend to notice high frequency interference more than the low frequency variety. However, if you switch in the low frequency filtering, you will normally notice a very marked drop in the background noise level. It is a case of not being fully aware of the problem when it is there, but noticing its absence when it has gone! High frequency interference is usually the more severe kind, but it is probably worthwhile tackling the low frequency type as well.

Figure 2.1 shows the circuit diagram for the lowpass filter. This is a conventional three stage (18dB per octave) active type. IC1 merely operates as a buffer amplifier at the input of the circuit, which ensures that the filter circuit is fed from a suitably low source impedance. IC2 is used as the buffer amplifier in the main filter circuit. The component values in the filter network gives a −6dB cutoff frequency of approximately 2.5kHz.

The circuit diagram of the highpass filter appears in Figure 2.2. This is basically the same as the lowpass filter, but

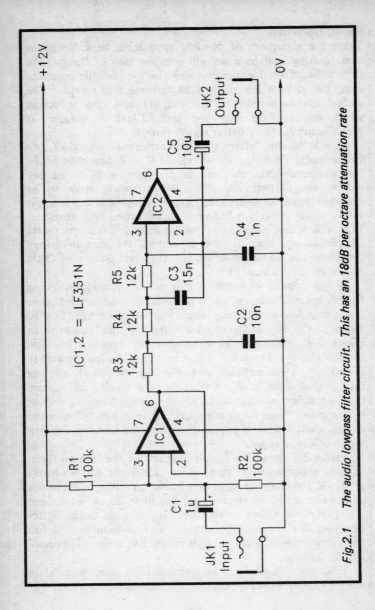

Fig.2.1   The audio lowpass filter circuit.   This has an 18dB per octave attenuation rate

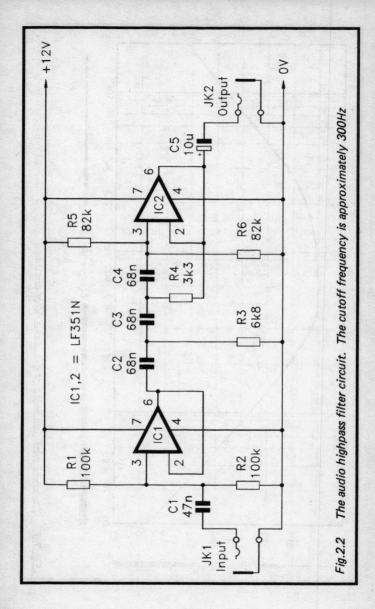

Fig.2.2 The audio highpass filter circuit. The cutoff frequency is approximately 300Hz

27

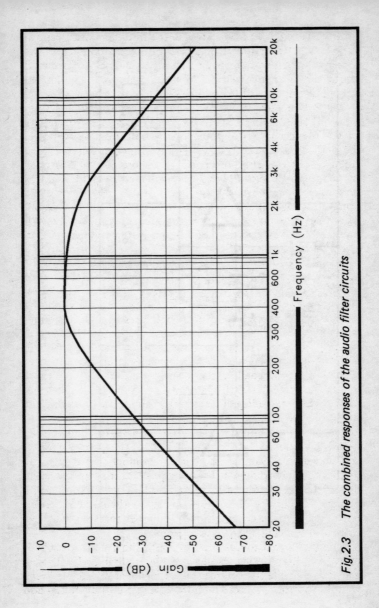

Fig.2.3   The combined responses of the audio filter circuits

28

with the resistors and capacitors in the filter network swapped over so that the required highpass filtering is obtained. The component values have been chosen to give a −6dB cutoff frequency of about 300Hz. Figure 2.3 shows the combined frequency response of the two filters.

These two filter circuits are shown as being powered from a 12 volt supply in the circuit diagrams. Some receivers have a 12 volt power supply output which could be used to power the filters. Alternatively, a 12 volt mains power supply circuit could be used as the power source. There is a third alternative in the form of batteries. A 9 volt battery such as a PP3 type is just about adequate, but I would not recommend using a supply voltage of less than 9 volts. The circuit will work properly on supply potentials of up to 30 volts, but there is no advantage in using a supply potential of more than about 12 to 15 volts.

With these two audio filter circuits, and the others featured in this book, it is assumed that the output will be fed to headphones. For DXing it is generally accepted that headphones are better than loudspeaker operation. Headphones tend to cut you off from distracting noises in your surroundings, and make it easier to concentrate on the received signals. Anyway, the receiver audio filter circuits featured here will drive most types of headphones properly, but can not drive even a high impedance loudspeaker without the assistance of a power amplifier circuit.

With high impedance headphones (about 1k to 4k) results will probably be best if the phones are wired in parallel. With low and medium impedance headphones (8R to about 600R) results will almost certainly be best with the phones connected in series. Some headphones are much more sensitive than others. With higher sensitivity types it may be beneficial to add a resistor of a few hundred ohms in series with the phones. Otherwise it may be found that the volume control has to be adjusted very carefully in order to avoid excessive volume and ringing in the ears!

The best signal source for the unit is the headphone socket of the receiver. This should provide a suitable signal level, and it will enable the volume to be controlled via the receiver's volume control. A 3 or 8 ohm loudspeaker output should also

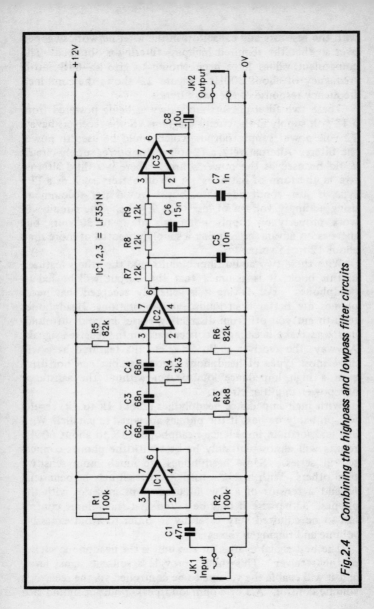

Fig.2.4 Combining the highpass and lowpass filter circuits

be suitable. A tape output is less than ideal. The output level might be inadequate to drive most headphones, and the receiver's volume control will not affect the output level from the tape socket.

If both filters are used, you could simply leave the circuits unaltered and wire the output of the highpass filter to the input of the lowpass type. This is doing things the hard way though. Figure 2.4 shows how the two filters can be direct coupled. This enables C5 and JK2 in the highpass filter to be omitted, as well as IC1, JK1, C1, R1, and R2 in the lowpass filter.

Components for Lowpass Filter (Fig.2.1)

Resistors (all 0.25 watt 5% carbon film)

R1	100k
R2	100k
R3	12k
R4	12k
R5	12k

Capacitors

C1	1μ 63V elect
C2	10n polyester 5%
C3	15n polyester 5%
C4	1n polyester 5%
C5	10μ 25V elect

Semiconductors

IC1	LF351N
IC2	LF351N

Miscellaneous

JK1	Standard jack socket
JK2	Standard jack socket
	8 pin d.i.l. i.c. holder (2 off)
	Circuit board, case, wire, solder, etc.

Components for Highpass Filter (Fig.2.2)

Resistors (all 0.25 watt 5% carbon film)

R1	100k
R2	100k
R3	6k8
R4	3k3
R5	82k
R6	82k

Capacitors

C1	47n polyester
C2	68n polyester 5%
C3	68n polyester 5%
C4	68n polyester 5%
C5	10μ 25V elect

Semiconductors

IC1	LF351N
IC2	LF351N

Miscellaneous

JK1	Standard jack socket
JK2	Standard jack socket
	8 pin d.i.l. i.c. holder (2 off)
	Circuit board, case, wire, solder, etc.

Components for Highpass/Lowpass Filter (Fig.2.4)

Resistors (all 0.25 watt 5% carbon film)

R1	100k
R2	100k
R3	6k8
R4	3k3
R5	82k
R6	82k
R7	12k
R8	12k
R9	12k

Capacitors

C1	47n polyester
C2	68n polyester 5%
C3	68n polyester 5%
C4	68n polyester 5%
C5	10n polyester 5%
C6	15n polyester 5%
C7	1n polyester 5%
C8	10μ 25V elect

Semiconductors

IC1	LF351N
IC2	LF351N
IC3	LF351N

Miscellaneous

JK1	Standard jack socket
JK2	Standard jack socket
	8 pin d.i.l. i.c. holder (3 off)
	Circuit board, case, wire, solder, etc.

Bypass Switch

When band conditions are good you may prefer to switch out the filtering. All that is needed is a d.p.d.t. switch connected as shown in Figure 2.5. If the filter is built as an external unit which has its own built-in battery supply, then the bypass and on/off switch functions could be combined in a single switch. A two way three pole type would be required. Note that this method of bypass switching is applicable to all the receiver audio filters featured in this book.

L – C Audio Filter

A passive filter based on an L – C network can provide a very high level of performance from a reasonably simple circuit. The problem with a filter of this type is that it requires fairly high value inductors that will operate efficiently at audio frequencies. Ordinary r.f. chokes are unsuitable as these components normally only go up to values of about 10mH or so, whereas this application requires values from around

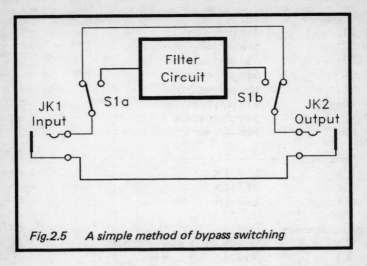

Fig.2.5   A simple method of bypass switching

10mH to a few hundred mH. Also, r.f. chokes are mostly designed to operate at frequencies above 100kHz, and are not likely to operate properly at audio frequencies. This is not just a matter of Q values being low at audio frequencies – they would in all probability provide completely different values at these lower frequencies!

The circuit featured in Figure 2.6 is based on an old filter configuration, but one which still provides excellent results in this application. I found that it will work quite well using inductors that are intended for operation at fairly low frequencies, but are not actually intended for operation over the audio range. Details of these are provided in the components list. The circuit should work just as well, or possibly a little better, using inductors that are specifically intended for operation at audio frequencies. However, these could be difficult or impossible to obtain, and would almost certainly be very expensive if suitable components could be traced. If you decide to use inductors that are not specifically intended for low frequency operation, other than the ones specified in the components list, bear in mind that they might not work properly in this circuit. Unfortunately, the only way to find out is to use the "suck it and see" approach.

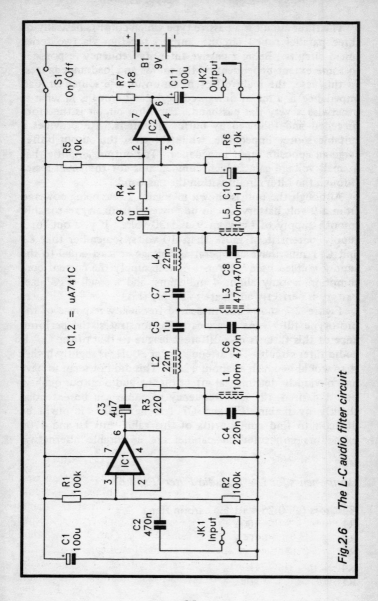

Fig.2.6   The L-C audio filter circuit

IC1,2 = uA741C

35

The filter circuit is a passive type which consists basically of three parallel tuned circuits coupled together via two series tuned circuits. Being a passive filter, its frequency response is to some extent dependent on the source and load impedances. In this case, the main effect of an unsuitable source or load impedance is a lot of unwanted peaks and troughs in what is otherwise a very flat passband. The filter circuit is therefore preceded and followed by buffer amplifiers. R3 provides a suitable source impedance, while R4 gives the output buffer stage an apposite input impedance. The output amplifier has a small voltage gain, which compensates for the small losses through the filter circuit within the passband.

Although the unit is shown in Figure 2.6 as being powered from a 9 volt battery, it can be powered from any reasonably smooth supply of between 9 and 30 volts. If you opt for a supply potential of more than 10 volts, remember that C1 and C11 must have an operating voltage at least equal to the supply voltage used. From a 9 volt supply the current consumption is only about 4 milliamps, and a small (PP3 size) battery is perfectly adequate to supply this.

Figure 2.7 shows the measured frequency response of the prototype filter. As this clearly demonstrates, the performance of this filter is in a different league to that of the C − R audio filter circuit. The attenuation at 300Hz is slightly higher than would be ideal, at about 12dB. This did not seem to have any obviously detrimental effect on the audio output quality, but if desired, the low frequency response can be extended slightly by making C5 and C7 $1\mu5$ in value. It might be difficult to find components of this value, but 1μ and 470n capacitors connected in parallel are a suitable alternative.

Components for L − C Audio Filter (Fig.2.6)

Resistors (all 0.25 watt 5% carbon film)

R1	100k
R2	100k
R3	220
R4	1k
R5	10k

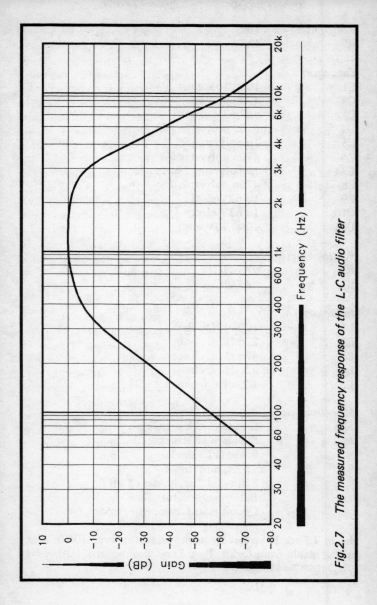

Fig. 2.7   The measured frequency response of the L-C audio filter

| R6 | 10k |
| R7 | 1k8 |

Capacitors
C1	100μ 10V elect
C2	470n polyester
C3	4μ7 63V elect
C4	220n polyester 5%
C5	1μ polyester 5%
C6	470n polyester 5%
C7	1μ polyester 5%
C8	470n polyester 5%
C9	1μ 63V elect
C10	1μ 63V elect
C11	100μ 10V elect

Semiconductors
| IC1 | μA741C |
| IC2 | μA741C |

Inductors
L1	100mH l.f. choke
L2	22mH l.f. choke
L3	47mH l.f. choke
L4	22mH l.f. choke
L5	100mH l.f. choke

Miscellaneous
JK1	Standard jack socket
JK2	Standard jack socket
B1	9 volt (PP3 size)
S1	s.p.s.t. min toggle
	8 pin d.i.l. i.c. holder (2 off)
	Battery connector
	Circuit board, case, wire, solder, etc.

L1 to L5 are Toko low frequency inductors type 10RB, which are available from Cirkit, Park Lane, Broxbourne, Herts EN10 7NQ (0992 441306).

C.W. Filter

Relatively few communications receivers seem to be equipped with an i.f. filter for c.w. (Morse) reception. With modern radio equipment a c.w. filter often seems to be an optional extra, but an expensive one which is not often fitted. An audio filter for c.w. reception represents a simple and inexpensive means of obtaining improved performance when using this mode. An audio c.w. filter can actually be very effective at reducing QRM. Over the years a number of communications receivers having built-in c.w. audio filters have been produced.

For optimum results quite a narrow bandwidth is required. Opinions vary as to what constitutes the ideal bandwidth for c.w. reception, but there is agreement that a narrow bandwidth of no more than a few hundred hertz is needed. In theory, a bandwidth of just a few hertz would suffice, since a c.w. signal contains just a single frequency (i.e. the carrier frequency). In practice things are not as simple as this. In the real world signals tend to drift in frequency. Even if your receiver is stable to within one hertz per hour, it is unlikely that many received signals would have anything approaching this degree of stability. With many receivers the drift is measured in kilohertz per hour rather than hertz per hour. With a very narrow bandwidth, constant retuning would probably be needed in order to keep received signals within the passband of the receiver.

Another problem with narrow bandwidths, especially if accompanied by high attenuation rates in the "skirts" of the filter, is that it can be difficult to tune in stations. Only a very small adjustment of the tuning dial is needed to tune straight through a signal and out the other side. Due to the intermittent nature of a c.w. signal you might not even hear a "bleep" as you tune through it. Having tuned in a station, it can be very easy to lose it again. With a very narrow bandwidth and sharp filtering everything becomes very fiddly and difficult.

You therefore have to choose a good compromise between a narrow enough bandwidth to provide good attenuation of adjacent channel interference, and a wide enough bandwidth to render the filter usable. The situation is similar with the attenuation rate of the filter. The attenuation rate must be low enough to enable signals to be easily tuned in and retained, but it must also be sufficiently high to give good attenuation of QRM. It is easy to produce a filter that has a very impressive looking frequency response, but which in use is more trouble than it is worth!

Having tried several c.w. audio filters over the years, my preference is certainly for one which errs on the side of caution, and has a relatively wide bandwidth. Most audio bandpass filters tend to naturally have a very narrow passband, and will only produce a somewhat wider bandwidth if they are designed to have low Q values. This gives the broader bandwidth, but also gives low attenuation rates in the "skirts" of the response.

A better way of obtaining a slightly broader bandwidth, and the one used in the circuit of Figure 2.8, is to use two filters operating on slightly different frequencies, and connected in series. In theory this gives a twin-peaked response, but in practice only a single peak will be obtained if the operating frequencies of the two filters are very close together. As can be seen from the frequency response graph of the prototype filter (Fig.2.9), in this case only a single peak is obtained.

Circuit Operation

IC1 acts as a buffer stage at the input of the unit. The main function of this stage is to ensure that the first filter circuit is fed from a suitably low impedance. R1 plus the input impedance of the input buffer amplifier (about 2.3k) reduce the input signal level by about 46dB. This attenuation is needed to compensate for the voltage gain through the two filter circuits, and it gives the circuit an overall voltage gain of about unity.

The two filter circuits use a standard operational amplifier bandpass arrangement. The operating frequency of each filter is governed by the values of the two filter capacitors and the two resistors. The Q of each filter is controlled by the ratio of one filter resistor value to the other. The operating frequency of the filter based on IC2 has been made slightly higher than the operating frequency of the filter based on IC3. This has been achieved by making R4 and R7 slightly lower in value than R8 and R9. The filters have a moderately high Q value,

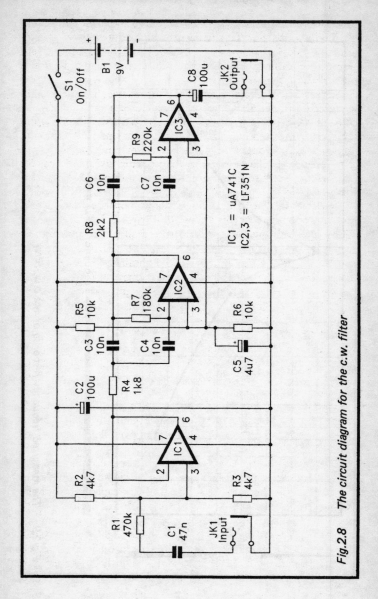

Fig.2.8   The circuit diagram for the c.w. filter

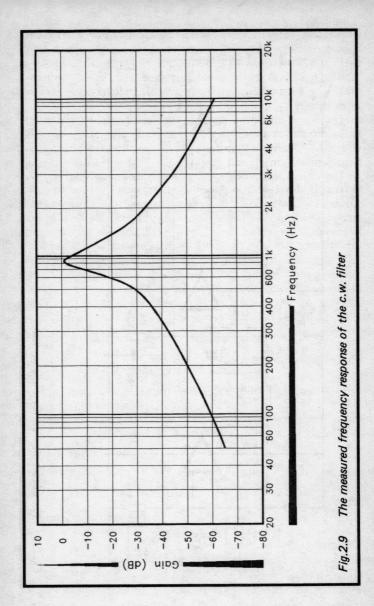

Fig.2.9   The measured frequency response of the c.w. filter

which gives good attenuation rates in the "skirts" of their responses. However, the Q has not been made so high that there are problems with noise and ringing effects. It is especially important to avoid ringing effects in this application, where "smearing" of a c.w. signal could severely reduce its intelligibility.

The notes on power supplies and use given for the audio filters described previously in this book also apply to this design. The current consumption of the circuit is about 4 to 5 milliamps from a 9 volt supply.

The centre frequency of the filter is at around 800 to 900 hertz. This is a middle audio frequency, which is about right for a c.w. tone. There is some advantage in using a higher frequency of around 2kHz or so, as explained in detail in the next section of this book, but most people find it more difficult to concentrate on a tone as high in pitch as that. Anyway, the centre frequency is easily changed, as it is inversely proportional to the value of C3, C4, C6, and C7. For instance, making these components 4n7 in value, would increase the centre frequency of the filter to about 2kHz. Note though, that changes in the filter's centre frequency result in changes in the bandwidth.

Components for C.W. Audio Filter (Fig.2.8)

Resistors (all 0.25 watt 5% carbon film)
R1	470k
R2	4k7
R3	4k7
R4	1k8
R5	10k
R6	10k
R7	180k
R8	2k2
R9	220k

Capacitors
C1	47n polyester
C2	100μ 10V elect
C3	10n polyester 5%

C4	10n polyester 5%
C5	4µ7 63V elect
C6	10n polyester 5%
C7	10n polyester 5%
C8	100µ 10V elect

Semiconductors

IC1	µA741C
IC2	LF351N
IC3	LF351N

Miscellaneous

S1	s.p.s.t. min toggle
JK1	Standard jack socket
JK2	Standard jack socket
B1	9 volt (PP3 size)
	8 pin d.i.l. i.c. holder (3 off)
	Battery connector
	Circuit board, case, wire, solder, etc.

Using Audio Filters

When using audio filters for s.s.b. or c.w. reception it is important to realise that an audio bandwidth of (say) 2.5kHz is not the same as having an intermediate frequency bandwidth of 2.5kHz. The important point to keep in mind here is that a signal 2.5kHz above the b.f.o. frequency will give a 2.5kHz audio output frequency, and so will one 2.5kHz below the b.f.o. frequency. With a high quality i.f. filter the b.f.o. is placed at one end of the filter's passband. It is placed at the upper end for lower sideband reception, or at the lower end for upper sideband reception.

If we consider the situation for lower sideband reception, it is as depicted in Figure 2.10. The b.f.o. is positioned at the upper end of the receiver's i.f. passband, and with a lower sideband signal correctly tuned in, that signal is totally within the i.f. passband. If there is any QRM on the opposite (upper) side of the b.f.o. signal, it is outside the receiver's passband, and is severely attenuated by the i.f. filtering.

With a receiver which has a bandwidth that is too wide for optimum s.s.b. reception you have a situation which is more

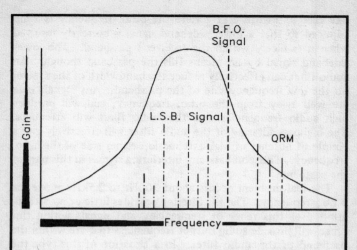

Fig.2.10   An L.S.B. signal within the receiver's passband, and some QRM on the other side of the b.f.o. frequency which is not

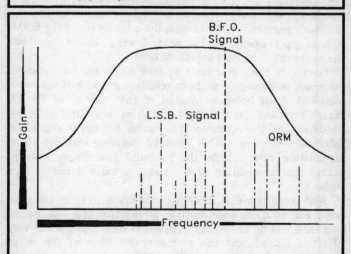

Fig.2.11   A wider i.f. bandwidth gives lower attenuation of the QRM

45

like that of Figure 2.11. Here the b.f.o. frequency is again adjusted so that a lower sideband signal is correctly resolved when it is nicely within the receiver's passband. The lower sideband signal by no means fills the passband though. An audio filter can effectively reduce the bandwidth of the system on the low frequency side of the passband. Any signals here are well away from the b.f.o. frequency, and will produce high audio frequencies that the audio filter will attenuate. The highpass filtering of the audio filter will effectively give a couple of notches of high attenuation either side of the b.f.o. frequency. This combats any interfering signals in this part of the passband.

The real problem occurs about 300Hz to 2.5kHz above the b.f.o. frequency. The i.f. filtering provides little or no attenuation over this range of frequencies, and signals within this range will provide audio output frequencies that are within the passband of the audio filter. In a situation of this type the audio filter will be most effective with the b.f.o. frequency pushed as far into the "skirts" of the filter's response as you can reasonably go. As Figure 2.12 shows, increasing the b.f.o. frequency still leaves the lower sideband signal within the receiver's passband, but increases the attenuation of the QRM. A large gap is opened up below the lower sideband signal, but the audio filter combats any QRM here.

Obviously there is a limit to how much the b.f.o. can be increased in frequency without resulting in some of the lower sideband signal being attenuated in the "skirts" of the i.f. filter's response. It is really a matter of using trial and error to determine the optimum frequencies for upper and lower sideband reception. With poor i.f. filtering that has a low attenuation rate outside the passband you simply have to accept that attenuation of the image signal will not be very high.

With a receiver that has a high quality a.m. filter, the passband will be quite wide, but the attenuation rate outside the passband will be quite high. An audio filter can then be very effective indeed, and the average attenuation of the image should be quite high (probably 40dB or more). In the case of a direct conversion receiver there is no i.f. filtering to attenuate the image response. With a receiver of this type you

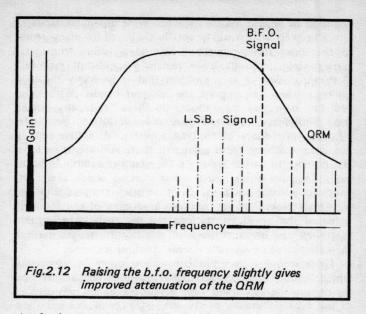

Fig.2.12   Raising the b.f.o. frequency slightly gives improved attenuation of the QRM

simply have to accept that it will receive equally well on either side of the b.f.o. frequency. This is the price that has to be paid for the simplicity of direct conversion sets.

Although I have been talking here in terms of audio filters used to aid s.s.b. reception, the situation is similar for c.w. reception. Matters are actually slightly better in that there are two peaks of sensitivity about 900Hz either side of the b.f.o. frequency. With the two responses a relatively generous 1.8kHz apart it is easier to obtain good attenuation of the image response. If the receiver has a good quality s.s.b. filter you may be able to obtain around 60dB of image attenuation. It is again a matter of experimenting to find the b.f.o. frequency that gives best results.

Notch Filter
The increased use of single sideband and reduced use of ordinary a.m. has to some extent lessened the problem of QRM in the form of heterodyne "whistles". It is a problem that has not completely disappeared though. Although a.m.

47

is due to be phased out on the short wave broadcast bands, it seems unlikely that it will be totally abolished for many years. In the mean time, unwanted heterodyne tones from a.m. carrier waves seem likely to remain a significant problem.

Paradoxically, it is a problem that is probably most in evidence when listening on the amateur bands. With s.s.b. and c.w. being the main modes on these bands, any carrier wave within the receiver's passband will interact with the b.f.o. to produce a heterodyne whistle. Although a.m. is not used much by radio amateurs, there still seems to be a fair number of carrier waves on the amateur bands. In some cases these are from non-amateur stations which share the bands, or intrude on them. In other cases it is probably due to signals picked up on spurious responses of the receiver. Some of the broadcast stations put out such strong signals that they can break through at significant strength even if they are picked up on quite a weak spurious response.

There seems to be a problem with some modern receivers which actually pick up internally generated signals. If you disconnect the aerial and tune across the bands, any signals of this type are usually pretty weak. On the other hand, they can still cause problems when listening to weak DX stations, and there are sometimes a few internally generated signals that are quite strong.

An audio filter can be very good indeed at combating heterodynes. The degree of attenuation available varies some what from one design to another, and with most notch filters it depends to a large extent on how well (or otherwise) you adjust the controls. Most designs offer at least 40dB of attenuation, and many can provide more than double this if they are carefully set up. I found that with the design featured here (Fig.2.13) an attenuation of over 80dB could be achieved if it was adjusted carefully.

With this degree of attenuation it is possible to render a signal fully readable, even if previously it was totally unreadable due to a strong heterodyne. The only problem is that the heterodyne will probably activate an a.g.c. system, and this will result in a reduced audio output level from the wanted signal. However, a weak but whistle-free signal will be easily

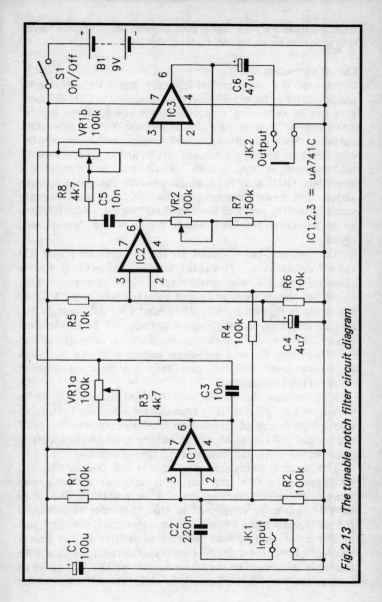

Fig.2.13   The tunable notch filter circuit diagram

49

read, whereas a strong signal plus an even stronger heterodyne will probably be completely unreadable.

Circuit Operation

Circuits of this type are traditionally based on a transistor phase-splitter. In other words, a transistor which operates as a sort of combined emitter follower and common emitter amplifier, so that it provides anti-phase signals from two outputs. Such circuits work well enough, but in my experience tend to be slightly unpredictable, and can need a lot of readjustment in use. This circuit has two operational amplifiers (IC1 and IC2) which provide the phase splitter action, and more consistent results. IC1 is a non-inverting amplifier which provides the "in-phase" signal, while IC2 acts as an inverting amplifier which produces the "anti-phase" signal.

The two anti-phase signals are fed to buffer amplifier IC3 via a Wien network. This is the same sort of network that is commonly used in high quality audio signal generators. One section of the network is formed by R3, VR1a, and C3, while the other is formed by R8, VR1b, and C5. At a certain frequency, and only at this frequency, there will be an identical phase shift through the two sections of the network, and at this frequency the two anti-phase signals will tend to cancel each other out. It is this cancelling that gives the required notch of high attenuation.

VR2 enables the closed loop voltage gain of IC2 to be varied, and in practice it is adjusted for optimum balance so that a high degree of attenuation is obtained at the centre of the notch. VR1 controls the frequency at which the identical phase shift occurs, and thus acts as a tuning control.

The current consumption of the circuit is only about 5 milliamps, so a PP3 size battery is adequate as the power source. When constructing the unit, note that the two gangs of VR1 should be connected so that they operate in unison (i.e. as the resistance of one section is increased, the resistance of the other gang should increase as well). In the past a number of readers seem to have experienced problems with this type of circuit as they have connected the two gangs so that as the resistance of one increases, the resistance of the other decreases. Possibly the confusion has arisen due to the anti-phase signals in the Wien network. Anyway, it is the signals that are in anti-phase, not the two gangs of VR1.

VR1 provides a tuning range that extends from around 150Hz to approximately 3.6kHz. With receivers that have a wide bandwidth a wider tuning range would be desirable. The high frequency coverage can be extended by making R3 and R8 lower in value, and the low frequency coverage can be increased by making VR1 higher in value. For example, a value of 2k2 for R3 and R8, plus a value of 220k for VR1, would give a coverage of around 70Hz to 7.5kHz. However, making the frequency coverage wider makes accurate tuning of the unit somewhat more tricky.

In use the first step is to tune VR1 to reduce the heterodyne as much as possible. Then VR2 is adjusted to optimise the attenuation. In order to obtain really high levels of attenuation it is usually necessary to repeat this process a few times. It should be possible to render any heterodyne inaudible after some careful adjustment of these two controls.

With some receivers it might be found that on removing the heterodyne, a higher-pitched tone can be heard. This tone, if present at all, should be at a relatively low level, and is caused by harmonic distortion in the detector and audio stages of the receiver. This signal is a harmonic or harmonics of the notched-out tone. There is not a great deal that can be done about it, but fortunately this problem is totally absent or barely noticeable when a notch filter is used with the vast majority of receivers.

Figure 2.14 shows the measured frequency response of the prototype notch filter when adjusted for a centre frequency of approximately 1kHz and a maximum attenuation of about 80dB. Obviously there is some attenuation of any signals close to the notch frequency. In practice though, the effect on the subjective audio quality is not very great, and the notch is narrow enough to give good results.

Components for Tunable Notch Filter (Fig.2.13)

Resistors (all 0.25 watt 5% carbon film)
R1   100k

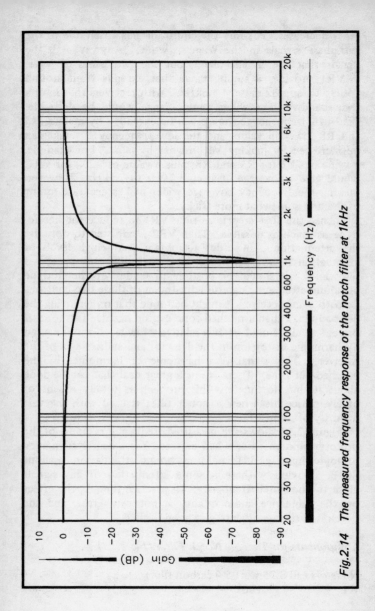

Fig.2.14 The measured frequency response of the notch filter at 1kHz

R2	100k
R3	4k7
R4	100k
R5	10k
R6	10k
R7	150k
R8	4k7

Potentiometers

VR1	100k lin dual gang
VR2	100k lin

Capacitors

C1	100µ 10V elect
C2	220n polyester
C3	10n polyester
C4	4µ7 63V elect
C5	10n polyester
C6	47µ 16V elect

Semiconductors

IC1	µA741C
IC2	µA741C
IC3	µA741C

Miscellaneous

S1	s.p.s.t. min toggle
B1	9 volt (PP3 size)
JK1	Standard jack socket
JK2	Standard jack socket
	8 pin d.i.l. i.c. holder (3 off)
	Battery connector
	Two control knobs
	Circuit board, case, wire, solder, etc.

Parametric Equaliser

A parametric equaliser is a device which is associated more with the electronic music business than with short wave radio. In fact the circuit featured here (Fig.2.15) is a slightly simplified version of the one featured in my book "More Advanced

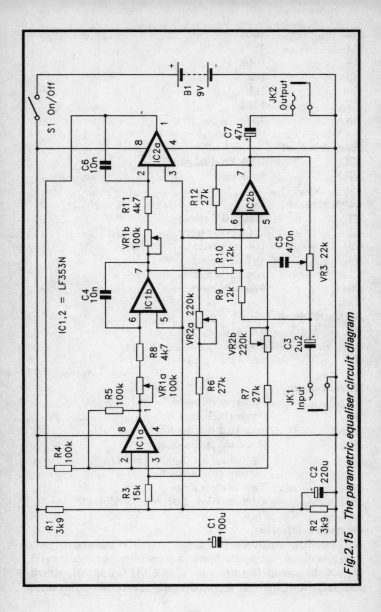

Fig.2.15 The parametric equaliser circuit diagram

54

Electronic Music Projects" (BP174). A unit of this type is basically a sort of super tone control, which can be used to provide bass cut, middle boost, or practically anything you require.

In a short wave reception context it can obviously be useful to be able to attenuate a band of frequencies that are infested with interference. For removing a single frequency the notch filter described previously is the better way of handling things, but these days interference from marine beacon stations, etc., is not necessarily in the form of a keyed carrier wave. It is often in the form of a two-tone signal, or some kind of complex signal that occupies a narrow range of frequencies rather than just one frequency. A notch filter can often be quite effective at combating this type of interference, as it obviously covers a small band of frequencies. A parametric equaliser can be more effective though, since it enables the width of the notch to be adjusted.

When used to provide boost a parametric equaliser can act as a c.w. audio filter. It is just a matter of setting it for a narrow bandwidth and maximum boost. I suppose that with an a.m. or s.s.b. signal under noisy conditions it might be possible to improve the intelligibility of a signal by boosting a certain range of frequencies. The only way to exploit a versatile unit of this type is to experiment a little to see what can be achieved.

Circuit Operation
This is a fairly complex form of filter, but looking at things in basic terms, a state variable filter is formed by IC1a, IC1b, and IC2a. In this application the filter is only used in the bandpass mode. IC2b operates as a conventional summing mode mixer circuit which combines the direct input signal and the filtered signal. It can give either in-phase mixing to produce a bandpass action, or out-of-phase mixing to give notch filtering.

There are three controls which must be properly understood in order to use the filter properly. VR1 is simply a tuning control, and it enables the centre frequency of the filter to be adjusted from approximately 150Hz at maximum resistance to 3kHz at minimum resistance. VR3 provides

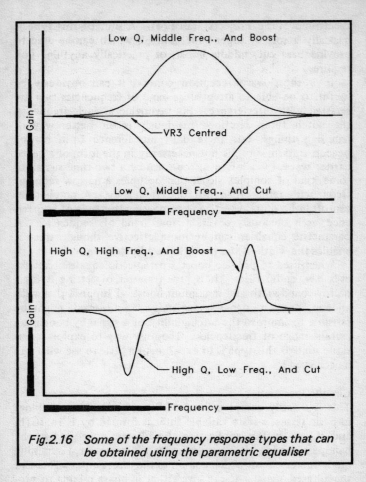

Fig.2.16 Some of the frequency response types that can be obtained using the parametric equaliser

boost with its wiper set towards the C3 end of its track, or cut if its wiper is set towards the end of the track which connects to IC2b's output. The response is flat over the audio range with the wiper of VR2 at the middle of the track, regardless of the settings of the other two controls. The degree of boost and cut available is to some extent dependent on the Q of the filter, but it is around 15dB.

The Q of the filter is controlled by VR2. Maximum resistance through VR2 gives maximum Q value. The Q value determines how wide or narrow a range of frequencies is affected by the filtering. A high Q gives a narrow bandwidth — a low Q gives a wide bandwidth. Figure 2.16 shows the types of response obtained at several control settings, and this should help to clarify the effects of the three controls.

Components for Parametric Equaliser (Fig.2.15)

Resistors (all 0.25 watt 5% carbon film)

R1	3k9
R2	3k9
R3	15k
R4	100k
R5	100k
R6	27k
R7	27k
R8	4k7
R9	12k
R10	12k
R11	4k7
R12	27k

Potentiometers

VR1	100k lin dual gang
VR2	220k lin dual gang
VR3	22k lin

Capacitors

C1	100µ 10V elect
C2	220µ 10V elect
C3	2µ2 63V elect
C4	10n polyester
C5	470n polyester
C6	10n polyester
C7	47µ 25V elect

Semiconductors

IC1	LF353N
IC2	LF353N

Miscellaneous

S1	s.p.s.t. min toggle
B1	9 volt (PP3 size)
JK1	Standard jack socket
JK2	Standard jack socket
	8 pin d.i.l. i.c. holder (2 off)
	Battery connector
	Three control knobs
	Circuit board, case, wire, solder, etc.

C.W./RTTY Decoder

RTTY (radio teletype) and c.w. have made something of a revival in recent years. One of the main reasons for this must be the popularity of computers amongst those who are interested in short wave radio. Although traditionally radio teletype is handled by huge and largely mechanical decoders, it is something that can be handled well using a computer. The output is displayed on the monitor, but can be also directed to a printer if hard copy is required. A setup of this type is actually a considerable advance on the old tele-type machines, which are now well and truly obsolete.

Morse code is a means of communication that is normally encoded and decoded by the operators, but it is again something that can be handled quite well by computers. Decoding morse signals is actually a bit more difficult than you might think. It is quite easy for a computer based system to recognise the letter patterns produced by another computer, which will produce code with perfect timing. Morse code generated by a human operator, even a good one, tends to be far less accurate. To a human morse code operator this is not important, as their pattern recognition algorithms seem to be able to cope with this.

Presumably the human brain does not achieve the decoding by analysing the sounds in terms of their strict timing, but instead looks for basic rhythms. For example, provided dots are substantially shorter than dashes, their precise relative durations are unimportant. The relatively small differences in duration will give the required rhythmic sound that can be decoded. Much of the early morse decoding software relied too heavily on looking for precise timing information in the signals, and did not provide very good results in most cases. In fact some sample printouts from an early morse decoder that I was shown some years ago contained one or two errors in practically. every word. Fortunately, most modern morse decoding software is more tolerant of ragged timing in the signal, and will decode most manually generated code with a fair degree of accuracy.

There is not really sufficient space available here for a detailed description of morse and RTTY decoding techniques. Also, it is difficult to be specific about using RTTY and c.w. tone decoders when there are so many different computers in use. Before building the tone decoder circuit featured here (Fig.2.17) you need to be sure about two things.

First, you must be certain that you can interface the unit to your computer successfully. This tone decoder provides an output at 0 and 5 volt logic levels, and it can drive any normal 5 volt logic input (TTL, CMOS, LS TTL, etc.). It can drive digital inputs such as those found on the user ports of some computers, or inputs on an add-on PIO port. It can not be guaranteed to operate an RS232C or similar input as these require input signals at logic levels of plus and minus 3 to 12 volts. A suitable line driver circuit would be needed in order to be certain that the unit could drive an input of this type. However, at the low baud rates involved in this application, and provided only a short connecting cable is used, most RS232C inputs can be driven successfully from a unit such as this one.

Secondly, you must be sure that you can obtain or write suitable decoder software. Morse and RTTY software is available for many computers, either as normal commercial software or from shareware/public domain libraries. The main point to watch when obtaining software of this type is that it is compatible with this tone decoder. Some morse and RTTY software seems to interface to the receiver via unusual routes that require non-standard hardware. Morse and RTTY software is not too difficult to write yourself. The RTTY type is particularly easy if the signal is decoded to parallel data by a UART, and interfaced via a parallel port. The program then has to do little more than convert the incoming five bit codes to their corresponding ASCII codes,

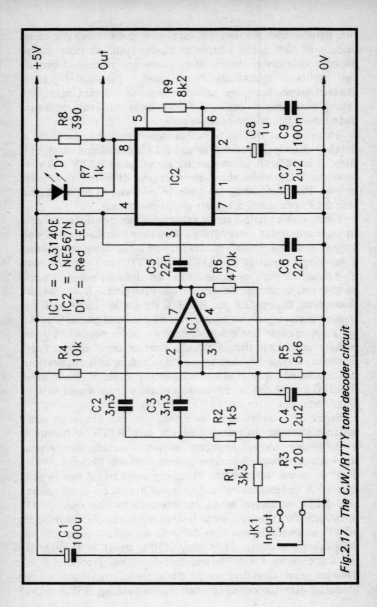

Fig.2.17 The C.W./RTTY tone decoder circuit

IC1 = CA3140E
IC2 = NE567N
D1 = Red LED

and display them on the screen. A UART for decoding amateur RTTY signals is described in the next section of this book incidentally.

Circuit Operation

The most simple method of tone decoding is to use a special phase locked loop integrated circuit, and this is the method utilized in this case. IC2 is an NE567N phase locked loop which is primarily intended for applications of this type. R9 and C9 are the timing components in the voltage controlled oscillator. These set the centre frequency at about 1.5kHz or so. C8 is the capacitive element in the lowpass filter (the resistor is an internal component of IC2).

Getting the phase locked loop to lock onto an incoming signal is one thing, getting this to produce a switching action is quite another. The method used by the NE567N is a form of synchronous detection. The v.c.o. is used to operate an electronic switch which is only turned on during positive output half cycles. The output signal from this switch is fed to smoothing capacitor C7. When the v.c.o. is locked onto the input signal, the two signals will be on the same frequency and in-phase with one another. The output from the switch is therefore a series of positive half cycles, which are smoothed to a reasonably ripple-free positive d.c. signal by C7.

This signal is used to operate an open collector switching transistor. When lock is not achieved, the input signal, if any, will be randomly phased in relation to the v.c.o. The output from the switch will then be a random selection of positive and negative signals. These are smoothed by C7 to produce no significant output voltage of either polarity. The output transistor therefore remains switched off.

The output terminal is therefore normally high, and is taken low when lock is achieved. R8 is the collector load resistor for the output transistor. D1 is a l.e.d. indicator which is switched on when the unit locks onto an input signal. In use this is useful as a sort of tuning indicator. C6 is a supply decoupling capacitor, and this should be mounted as close to IC2 as possible. C5 provides d.c. blocking at the input of the decoder.

C5 could be connected to the input socket, so that IC2 would be driven by an unprocessed input signal. The NE567N is quite an efficient device, with a narrow lock-on range, but even so, this would probably not give particularly good results in practice. Results are much better if IC2 is preceded by a bandpass filter so that the noise and interference which reaches the decoder is greatly reduced. IC1 is used in a simple bandpass filter having a centre frequency of approximately 1.5kHz. Note that the non-symmetrical biasing of IC1 is deliberate, and is needed due to the low supply voltage and the non-symmetrical output characteristics of IC1.

There is a high voltage gain of 40dB or so through the filter circuit at the centre of the passband. This makes the unit rather oversensitive. To avoid problems with overloading, an attenuator is used at the input of the unit. This also ensures that the bandpass filter is fed from a suitably low source impedance.

Results should be satisfactory using the specified values, but they might be something less than optimum. Ideally R9 should be replaced with a 5k6 fixed resistor in series with a 4k7 preset. The preset is then adjusted so that the free-running v.c.o. frequency is equal to the centre frequency of the bandpass filter. However, unless you have suitable test gear to permit the preset to be given the optimum setting, it is probably best just to use an 8k2 fixed resistor for R9.

The circuit consumes about 8 milliamps under standby conditions, and about 28 milliamps when the output transistor is switched on. Most computers have a 5 volt supply output that can easily handle this sort of current drain. Alternatively, a 5 volt supply can be derived from a 9 volt battery using the simple regulator circuit of Figure 2.18. It is advisable to use a fairly high capacity battery, such as six HP7 size cells in a plastic holder.

When constructing the unit, bear in mind that CA3140E used for IC1 has a PMOS input stage. It therefore requires the standard anti-static handling precautions.

In use, and when decoding c.w. signals, the receiver is tuned so that IC2 locks onto the incoming signal. Correct tuning will be indicated by D1 flashing on and off in sympathy with the audio tone from the c.w. signal. An RTTY signal is a two tone

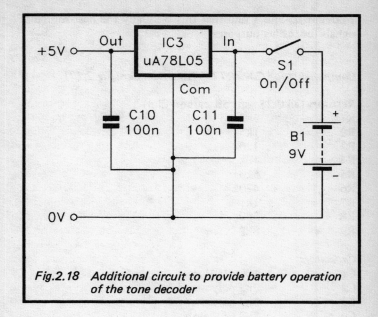

Fig.2.18 *Additional circuit to provide battery operation of the tone decoder*

type, with one tone being used for logic 0, and the other being used for logic 1. This gives the characteristic warbling sound from the headphones as the signal rapidly alternates between the two audio tones. Most amateur RTTY uses a tone shift of just 175Hz. Despite the fact that the phase locked loop is operating at a fairly high frequency of around 1.5kHz, it is still well able to lock onto one tone while ignoring the other one. Simply tune the receiver to lock onto one of the tones. If this gives a garbled output, it probably means that the polarity of the output signal is incorrect. An optional inverter could be included in the unit to correct this, but there is a simple alternative. Just retune the receiver so that the decoder locks onto the other tone.

RTTY signals are mainly to be found towards the low frequency end of each short wave amateur band. The 80 metre band will often provide some RTTY signals just below 3.6MHz. When conditions on the 20 metre band are reasonable there are usually a number of RTTY signals at around

14.090MHz, and I find that this is usually the best source of signals for testing purposes.

Components for C.W./RTTY Tone Decoder (Fig.2.17)

Resistors (all 0.25 watt 5% carbon film)

R1	3k3
R2	1k5
R3	120
R4	10k
R5	5k6
R6	470k
R7	1k
R8	390
R9	8k2

Capacitors

C1	100μ 10V elect
C2	3n3 polyester 5%
C3	3n3 polyester 5%
C4	2μ2 63V elect
C5	22n polyester
C6	22n ceramic
C7	2μ2 63V elect
C8	1μ 63V elect
C9	100n polyester 5%

Semiconductors

IC1	CA3140E
IC2	NE567N
D1	Red panel l.e.d.

Miscellaneous

JK1	Standard jack socket
	8 pin d.i.l. i.c. holder (2 off)
	Circuit board, case, wire, solder, etc.

Additional components for battery operation (Fig.2.18)

IC3	μA78LO5 (+5V 100mA reg.)
C10	100n ceramic
C11	100n ceramic
S1	s.p.s.t. min toggle
B1	9 volt (six HP7 size cells in holder)
	Battery connector (PP3 type)

RTTY UART

One approach to decoding RTTY signals is to feed the output of the tone decoder into one line of a parallel port on the computer. Software routines are then used to decode the serial signals into parallel data, and the Baudot codes are then translated into corresponding ASCII characters using further software routines. An easier method is to feed the output of the tone decoder into an RS232C port on the computer, and to use the computer's built-in hardware to provide the conversion from serial to parallel data.

In practice this second method is not often a practical one with Baudot based RTTY. With ASCII or any system that uses seven or eight bit characters there will probably be no problem, and the computer will almost certainly be able to handle the word format in use. There is a major difficulty with Baudot based RTTY in that it uses five bit codes, plus a method of shifting which operates in a basic manner rather like that of a shift key on a typewriter or computer keyboard. The software can easily handle the shift process, but the five bit codes are beyond the capabilities of most computer serial interfaces. The word format used is one start bit, five data bits, one and half stop bits, and no parity bit.

There is a further problem in that the baud rates used are not widely supported. The standard baud rate for amateur RTTY transmissions used to be 45.45. This seems to be an odd choice, and I have never been able to ascertain why this particular rate was chosen. These days there is a trend for amateurs to use the more common baud rate of 50. A fair number of computer serial ports can handle a baud rate of 50, but I do not know of any that can accommodate a rate of 45.45. In any case, computer serial interface chips do not seem to be able to deal with the five bit word format.

General purpose serial interface devices can handle any word format, including the little used five or six bit types. These components are called UARTs (universal asynchronous receiver/transmitters). The industry standard UART is the 6402, and this is well suited to operation as a serial to parallel converter for use in computer based RTTY decoding systems. It can be controlled from the buses of a microprocessor, but it is equally well suited to stand-alone operation where it is programmed by having its control inputs simply tied to the appropriate logic levels.

A UART, as its name implies, can provide both serial to parallel and parallel to serial conversion using the receiver and transmitter sections respectively. In this case it is only the receiver section that is needed, and the transmitter part of the device is left completely unused.

Circuit Operation
Figure 2.19 shows the circuit diagram for a serial to parallel decoder based on a 6402 UART (IC1). On the computer side of the circuit there are five outputs which carry the parallel data to a parallel port of the computer. The upper three outputs (pins 7 to 5) are unused in this five bit application, but they can obviously be brought into action if you should wish to program the circuit for seven or eight bit operation. In addition to the data lines, the computer must provide two handshake lines. Data can not be read reliably from the interface unless the handshaking is implemented properly.

Handshake line 2 ("HS2") connects to the "data ready" output of IC1. This output goes high when a complete character has been received and decoded. The computer must monitor this line and read the next character from the interface only when this line has gone high. Unfortunately, reading the interface does not automatically reset the "data ready" output to the low state. This must be done by pulsing "HS1" low, so that the "data ready reset" input of IC1 is activated.

Some computer parallel ports have handshake lines that are specifically designed for this type of handshaking. Where such lines are available they will almost certainly represent the easiest method of handling the handshaking. However, there is no difficulty in using ordinary digital inputs and outputs

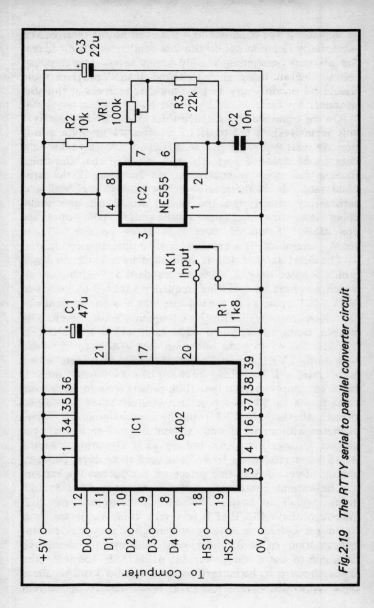

Fig.2.19 The RTTY serial to parallel converter circuit

to implement the handshaking. Data can not be received at a particularly fast rate due to the low baud rate in use. In fact the absolute maximum is only about seven characters per second. Even using an interpreted BASIC program there should be no difficulty in handling data received at this sort of speed.

On the input side of the circuit the serial data at ordinary 5 volt logic levels is fed to JK1. C1 and R1 generate a long positive reset pulse for IC1 at switch-on. For asynchronous data to be decoded correctly it is essential that the transmitting and receiving equipment are operating at the same baud rate. In fact errors of a few percent may well give satisfactory results, but the system would still give something less than optimum results under poor operating conditions. Errors of more than a few percent will give totally scrambled data even under ideal operating conditions.

The baud rate of IC1 is controlled by a clock oscillator which is based on IC2. This is a standard 555 astable circuit which can have its operating frequency adjusted by means of VR1. IC1 operates at a baud rate which is one-sixteenth of the clock frequency. The clock frequency must therefore be sixteen times the required baud rate, which works out at 727.2Hz for 45.45 baud operation, and 800Hz for 50 baud operation. VR1 can be adjusted to accommodate either baud rate. If switching between the two baud rates is required, simply include two 100k presets (one for each baud rate) plus a s.p.d.t. switch so that you can select the desired preset. Alternatively VR1 could be a panel mounted potentiometer with marks around the control knob to indicate the correct settings for 45.45 and 50 baud operation. As the 45.45 baud rate seems to be little used these days, you may simply prefer to have one preset set for 50 baud operation.

The current consumption of the circuit is about 8 milliamps, which is largely the current consumed by IC2. Although the 6402 UART is a very complex device, it is based on CMOS technology which gives a typical current consumption of well under one milliamp. It would be advisable to use a low power 555 (ICM7555, L555CP, etc.) if the circuit is to be battery powered via the 5 volt regulator circuit provided previously. This would reduce the current consumption of the circuit to little more than one milliamp. If the unit is to be powered from the computer, which will probably be the most convenient method in most cases, then an ordinary 555 should be perfectly satisfactory.

When constructing the circuit bear in mind that IC1 is a CMOS device which requires the standard anti-static handling precautions. Ideally VR1 should be given the correct setting with the aid of a frequency meter. VR1 is simply adjusted for an output frequency of 800Hz or 727.2Hz at pin 3 of IC2. Do not bother about getting the frequency correct to the nearest 0.01Hz. Provided the clock frequency is within a few hertz of the correct figure the unit should work well. Trial and error can be used to find a suitable setting if a suitable frequency meter is not available. Simply tune the system to an RTTY signal that is received at good strength and is reasonably free from QRM and QRN. Try VR1 at various settings until you find one that gives sensible output from the system. There will be a small range of settings that give acceptable results. Set VR1 in the middle of this range of settings.

Word Formats

As pointed out previously, the 6402 UART can handle any normal asynchronous serial communications word format. Details of how the device is programmed for various formats will be covered here so that, if necessary, you can set it up for other word formats. The word format is controlled by pins 34 to 39.

Pin 34 is taken high in order to load the data on pins 35 to 39 into the 6402's control register. In a stand-alone application this pin is normally just connected permanently to the +5 volt rail.

Pin 35 is the parity inhibit input. Take this terminal to logic 0 to enable parity checking, or to logic 1 if no parity is required.

Pin 36 is the stop bit select input. Take this to logic 0 for one stop bit or to logic 1 for two stop bits. Note that with five character word formats taking pin 36 high produces 1.5 stop bit operation.

Pins 37 and 38 are the character length inputs. The binary code on these inputs permits 5, 6, 7, or 8 bits of data to be accommodated. This operates in the manner shown in Table 1:

Table 1

PIN 37	PIN 38	DATA BITS
Logic 0	Logic 0	5
Logic 0	Logic 1	6
Logic 1	Logic 0	7
Logic 1	Logic 1	8

Pin 39 is the parity select input. Take this to logic 0 for odd parity or to logic 1 for even parity. Of course, if parity has been disabled by taking pin 35 high, then the logic level on Pin 39 is irrelevant.

Baudot Codes

Converting Baudot codes into equivalent ASCII codes (or whatever codes your computer uses) is not a difficult task. The usual method is to use a look-up table. In fact it will probably be necessary to use two look-up tables — one for the normal Baudot character set and the other for the shifted character set. Table 2 provides details of the Baudot code.

Components for RTTY Serial/Parallel Converter (Fig.2.19)

Resistors (all 0.25 watt 5% carbon film)
R1   1k8
R2   10k
R3   22k

Potentiometer
VR1   100k min hor preset

Capacitors
C1   47μ 10V elect
C2   10n polyester
C3   22μ 10V elect

Table 2

DECIMAL	HEX	LETTERS	FIGURES
0	00	Not used	Not used
1	01	E	3
2	02	Line feed	Line feed
3	03	A	—
4	04	Space	Space
5	05	S	Bell or '
6	06	I	8
7	07	U	7
8	08	Return	Return
9	09	D	$
10	0A	R	4
11	0B	J	' or bell
12	0C	N	,
13	0D	F	! or %
14	0E	C	:
15	0F	K	(
16	10	T	5
17	11	Z	"
18	12	L	)
19	13	W	2
20	14	H	£ or #
21	15	Y	6
22	16	P	0
23	17	Q	1
24	18	O	9
25	19	B	?
26	1A	G	& or +
27	1B	Figures	Figures
28	1C	M	.
29	1D	X	/
30	1E	V	;
31	1F	Letters	Letters

("Letters" and "Figures" are the two shift characters)

Semiconductors
IC1   6402 UART
IC2   NE555 (see text)

Miscellaneous
JK1   Standard jack socket
                   8 pin d.i.l. i.c. holder
                   40 pin d.i.l. i.c. holder
                   Circuit board, case, wire, solder, etc.

Speech Processor
This is the only project in this chapter which is intended to go
at the transmitting end of the system. There are plenty of
ways in which a signal can be improved at the receiving end of
the system, but there is not a great deal that can be done at
the transmitting end, other than making sure that the strongest
possible signal is transmitted. There are some processes that
can be applied to the signal though, and it is only fair to
point out that these processes are now an integral part of
many modern transmitters. Clearly there is no point in using
external speech processing with a transmitter that has effective built-in processing of this type. It is also only fair to
point out that some speech processing techniques can
substantially increase the power handled by the output stage
of the transmitter. Obviously this would not be acceptable
in some cases.

One approach to speech processing, and the most basic
one, is to use filtering to remove high and low frequencies.
These add little to the intelligibility of speech, particularly
the bass frequencies. This filtering is normally included in
transmitters in order to limit the bandwidth of their output
signal, so as to maximise the number of transmissions that can
be accommodated within each band.

Another, and more effective method, is to use compression.
If the waveform of a speech signal is analyzed it will be found
to contain frequent spiky sections. This means that the peak
power in the signal is very much higher than the average level.
The maximum strength of the transmitted signal is usually
limited by the peak level that the output stage can handle,
and not the average level. If the spiky peaks in the signal

could be clipped off, the average power level could be made much higher in relation to the peak level. This would effectively enable a stronger signal to be transmitted. The peak level would remain unaltered, but the average level (and the volume from the receiver) would be boosted.

Obviously some distortion of the signal must result from any processing of this type. However, clipping the spiky parts of the waveform has very much less effect than you might think. In fact there is little obvious change to the character of the processed voice provided the processing is done correctly. Provided the output stage of the transmitter can handle the higher average output power, a worthwhile increase in "talk-power" can be obtained. An effective increase of up to about 10dB can be produced.

The problem in using simple clipping of the signal to remove the spikes is that strong harmonic and intermodulation distortion are produced. The distortion products are almost certain to be so strong as to seriously degrade the intelligibility of the signal. Simple processing of this type would therefore be counter-productive.

The best speech processors use a fairly involved process which first has the signal converted to an s.s.b. type, after which it is clipped and then turned back to an audio signal again. Together with the appropriate filtering this virtually eliminates the distortion products. This method is rather complex and expensive though.

System Operation

A more simple alternative that can provide very good results is to use audio clipping plus high slope filtering. The block diagram of Figure 2.20 shows how this system operates.

The microphone feeds into a low noise preamplifier stage. A large amount of amplification is needed in order to bring the weak output signal from a microphone up to the level where it can be clipped using an ordinary diode clipper circuit. Consequently, the preamplifier drives a second amplifier stage via a gain control potentiometer. This control is used to set a suitable degree of compression.

The output of the second amplifier stage is fed to a high slope highpass filter. Harmonic distortion on middle and high

73

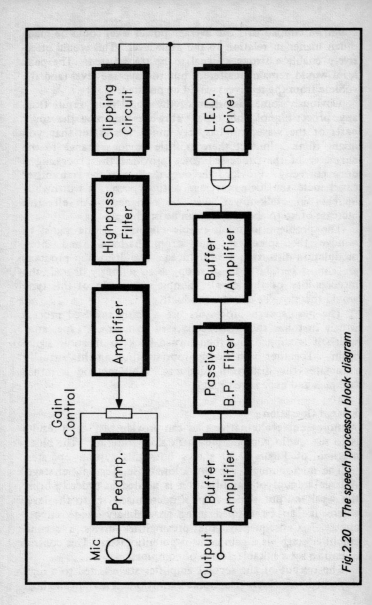

Fig.2.20   The speech processor block diagram

frequencies is not a major problem since most of the harmonics produced will be at fairly high frequencies, and can be easily filtered out. The low input frequencies are a very different matter. Low frequency input signals will produce harmonics right across the important 300Hz to 3kHz frequency range, and these signals can obviously not be filtered out. This problem can not be completely overcome in a reasonable simple audio frequency speech processor, but highpass filtering can be used to remove as much of the low frequency content as possible. Frequencies above the 300Hz cutoff frequency will produce some harmonics within the passband of the system, but relatively few of them. In a unit of this type a certain amount of distortion has to be tolerated.

A standard diode clipping circuit processes the output from the highpass filter. A simple l.e.d. driver circuit flashes a l.e.d. indicator when clipping is achieved. This is more than a little useful when adjusting the gain control. The next three stages of the unit are a buffer stage, a passive bandpass filter, and another buffer stage. The buffer stages are needed to ensure that the bandpass filter is fed from a suitable source impedance and that it feeds into an apposite load impedance.

Most of the distortion products generated by the clipping circuit will be at high audio frequencies, and it is mainly the lowpass filtering of the bandpass filter that cleans-up the output signal. However, there is a significant amount of low frequency distortion produced by intermodulation distortion. As intermodulation distortion tends to be very noticeable it is worthwhile using bandpass filtering rather than just opting for lowpass filtering.

Circuit Operation
Figures 2.21 to 2.23 show the circuit diagrams for the various stages of the circuit. The preamplifier has IC1 as an inverting amplifier with a voltage gain of about 40dB (100 times) and a nominal input impedance of 1k. This will suit most low impedance microphones, although with some types it might be beneficial to reduce R1 to about 390 ohms. This will reduce the input impedance and increase the voltage gain, which will give better results with very low impedance (about 200R) dynamic microphones. For operation with high

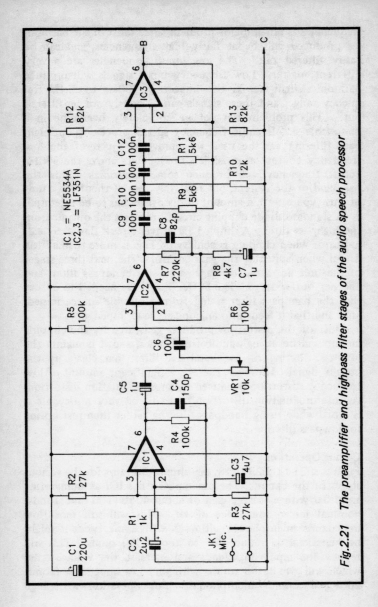

Fig.2.21   The preamplifier and highpass filter stages of the audio speech processor

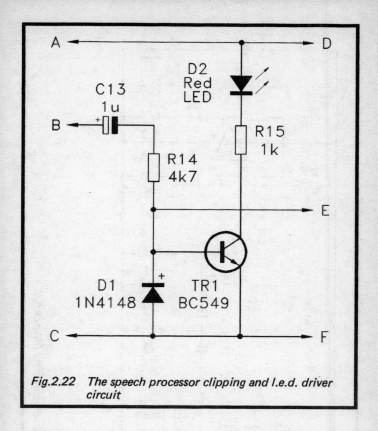

Fig.2.22 The speech processor clipping and l.e.d. driver circuit

impedance microphones R1 should be increased to about 22k in value. This will give a higher input impedance and reduce the gain of the circuit to a more appropriate level.

Note that the NE5534A specified for IC1 is a special low noise operational amplifier which is intended for use in low level audio circuits. The circuit will work properly using cheaper operational amplifiers such as the LF351N or µA741C, but the signal to noise ratio will be greatly degraded. In fact it could well be reduced by more than 20dB (by a factor of more than ten times). In a critical application such as this the extra cost of the NE5534A is probably well justified.

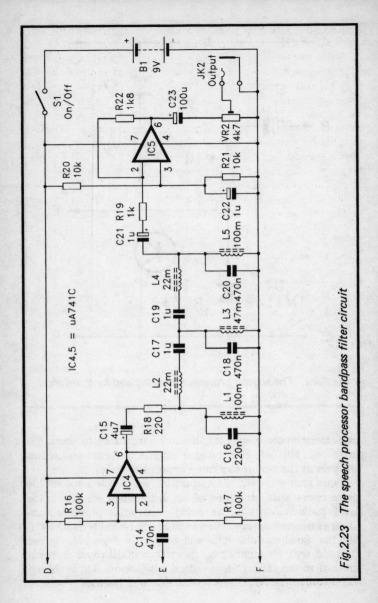

Fig.2.23 The speech processor bandpass filter circuit

VR1 is a standard volume control style gain control. Its output feeds into a non-inverting amplifier based on IC2, and having a voltage gain of roughly 34dB (50 times). C4 and C8 add a degree of lowpass filtering to the two amplifier stages. This helps to keep down the distortion products generated by the clipper circuit, but this filtering is far less important than the highpass filtering. The latter is provided by a fourth order (24dB per octave) active circuit based on IC3. This has a cutoff frequency of approximately 300Hz.

The clipper circuit is almost a standard twin silicon diode type providing hard clipping at about plus and minus 0.6 volts. It differs from the standard type only in that positive going signals are clipped by the base emitter junction of TR1 rather than a true diode. This is of no practical importance though. The point of using TR1 in the clipping circuit is that when driven into clipping it provides a current to l.e.d. indicator D2. This provides a simple but effective clipping level indication.

The bandpass filter requires little comment as it is identical to the receiver audio bandpass filter described previously. Its very high slope filtering provides this processor with excellent performance. I have tried a number of audio speech processor circuits over the years, and would certainly rate this one as the best I have encountered so far.

VR2 is an output attenuator. Ideally the unit would replace the microphone preamplifier in the transmitter, but presumably this will not be possible in most cases. If it is used as an out-board unit that connects between the microphone and the transmitter it will provide an output level that is far too high. VR2 is then adjusted to reduce the output level to one which is comparable to the output level of the microphone. If suitable test gear is available you can make some measurements so that the output level can be accurately matched to the microphone's output level. However, this is not essential and a bit of trial and error should do the job. The setting of VR2 should not be critical, and any setting which allows the transmitter to be driven correctly should be perfectly satisfactory.

The current consumption of the circuit is about 7 milli-amps. A small (PP3 size) battery is able to provide this, but if the unit is likely to be used for long periods I would recommend using a higher capacity battery. A PP9 size battery or six HP7 size cells in a plastic holder are suitable. The circuit will work from a 12 volt supply if necessary, but note that the supply must be very well smoothed or you could well find that the signal to noise ratio is just a few dB (with the noise not necessarily being the weaker signal!).

In use VR1 should be advanced just far enough to ensure that D2 lights quite brightly when you speak into the microphone. Resist the temptation to heavily clip the signal. Doing so will not give significantly more "talk-power" than moderate clipping, but will give very much higher distortion. Heavy clipping will certainly be counter-productive.

Components for Speech Processor (Figs.2.21, 2.22 and 2.23)

Resistors (all 0.25 watt 5% carbon film)

R1	1k (see text)
R2	27k
R3	27k
R4	100k
R5	100k
R6	100k
R7	220k
R8	4k7
R9	5k6
R10	12k
R11	5k6
R12	82k
R13	82k
R14	4k7
R15	1k
R16	100k
R17	100k
R18	220R
R19	1k
R20	10k
R21	10k
R22	1k8

Potentiometers

VR1	10k log
VR2	4k7 min hor preset

Capacitors

C1	220µ 16V elect
C2	2µ2 63V elect
C3	4µ7 63V elect
C4	150p ceramic plate
C5	1µ 63V elect
C6	100n polyester
C7	1µ 63V elect
C8	82p ceramic plate
C9	100n polyester
C10	100n polyester
C11	100n polyester
C12	100n polyester
C13	1µ 63V elect
C14	470n polyester
C15	4µ7 63V elect
C16	220n polyester 5%
C17	1µ polyester 5%
C18	470n polyester 5%
C19	1µ polyester 5%
C20	470n polyester 5%
C21	1µ 63V elect
C22	1µ 63V elect
C23	100µ 16V elect

Semiconductors

IC1	NE5534A
IC2	LF351N
IC3	LF351N
IC4	µA741C
IC5	µA741C
TR1	BC549
D1	1N4148
D2	Red panel l.e.d.

Miscellaneous

L1	100mH
L2	22mH
L3	47mH
L4	22mH
L5	100mH
S1	s.p.s.t. min-toggle
JK1	Standard jack, etc.
JK2	Standard jack, etc.
B1	9 volt (PP3 size – see text)
	Battery connector
	8 pin d.i.l. i.c. holder (5 off)
	Control knob
	Circuit board, case, wire, solder, etc.

Noise Limiters

A noise limiter is a simple form of clipping circuit that is used at the audio output of a receiver. The basic idea is to have a clipping level that is high enough for a signal at moderate volume to pass through unclipped, or with just slight clipping of the waveform peaks. Figure 2.24 shows how this cleans-up the signal by severely clipping strong noise spikes, but leaving the main signal unaffected.

I will not exaggerate the effectiveness of a simple clipping type noise limiters. Where very strong noise spikes are present there is genuinely a substantial improvement in the intelligibility of the signal. However, it will still be fairly heavily infested with noise, and far from easy to copy. Where the noise spikes are only at a low to medium level a noise limiter will not be of any benefit at all, since the noise spikes will not reach the clipping level.

In my experience one of the main benefits of using a noise limiter is that it will combat the deafening noise spikes that can occur with some communications receivers when using headphones. With a fair percentage of short wave sets someone switching on a light in the next room can cause a "click" through the headphones that is literally painful to the listener, and feels like it has induced cardiac arrest! A noise limiter can reduce such noise spikes to the point where they are annoying, but no more than this.

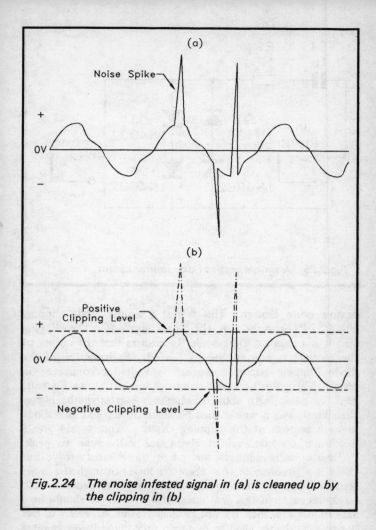

Fig.2.24 *The noise infested signal in (a) is cleaned up by the clipping in (b)*

Passive Limiter

In its most basic form a noise limiter is a purely passive circuit which connects between the output of the receiver and the headphones. Figure 2.25 shows the circuit diagram for a simple

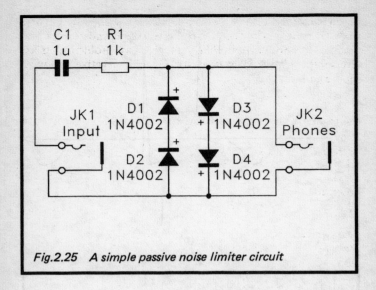

Fig.2.25 A simple passive noise limiter circuit

passive noise limiter. This is just a simple diode clipping circuit. C1 ensures that the signal applied to the clipping circuit is a true a.c. type while R1 ensures that the output of the receiver is not excessively loaded. Each section of the diode clipping circuit comprises two diodes connected in series. This gives a maximum output level of about 2.4 volts peak to peak. With some headphones this might be higher than ideal, and it would then be better to use just one diode in each section of the clipping circuit. This would give a maximum output level of about 1.2 volts peak to peak.

Passive noise limiters are often quite satisfactory, but there is a problem in that there are losses through the series resistor (R1). If the receiver has plenty of drive for the headphones, then this will not matter. If there should be a lack of volume, then R1 can be made lower in value. In fact it would probably need to be made very much lower in value in order to give satisfactory results with low impedance headphones. A value of about 10 ohms should be suitable for low impedance headphones. C1 would then need to be much higher in value — say about 47μ. It would also need to

84

be an electrolytic type, which in theory is not satisfactory since there would be no polarising voltage in most cases. In practice this would be unlikely to give any problems. If an electrolytic capacitor is used for C1, the negative terminal should connect to R1.

Components for Passive Noise Limiter (Fig.2.25)

Resistor
R1   1k 0.25 watt 5% carbon film

Capacitor
C1   1μ polyester

Semiconductors
D1   1N4002
D2   1N4002
D3   1N4002
D4   1N4002

Miscellaneous
JK1   Standard jack socket
JK2   Standard jack socket
                Case, circuit board, wire, solder, etc.

Active Noise Limiter
The circuit of Figure 2.25 can probably be made to work with practically any combination of receiver and headphones, albeit with some "tweaking" of the component values. More consistent results can be obtained using an active circuit such as the one shown in Figure 2.26. This has a clipping circuit much like the one in the passive noise limiter, but it is followed by a buffer amplifier having a high input impedance of over one megohm. This ensures that there are insignificant losses through R1, while the relatively high value of this component ensures that there is no risk of the receiver's output being loaded excessively. The circuit has a current consumption of only about 1 to 2 milliamps.

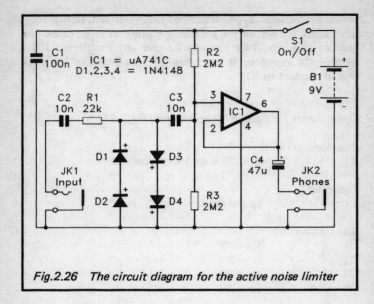

Fig.2.26   The circuit diagram for the active noise limiter

Components for Active Noise Limiter (Fig.2.26)

Resistors (all 0.25 watt 5% carbon film)
R1	22k
R2	2M2
R3	2M2

Capacitors
C1	100n ceramic
C2	10n polyester
C3	10n polyester
C4	47μ 10V elect

Semiconductors
IC1	μA741C
D1	1N4148
D2	1N4148
D3	1N4148
D4	1N4148

Miscellaneous

JK1	Standard jack socket
JK2	Standard jack socket
S1	s.p.s.t. min toggle
B1	9 volt (PP3 size)
	Battery connector
	8 pin d.i.l. i.c. holder
	Circuit board, case, wire, solder, etc.

Volume Expander

Volume expanders and noise gates are quite common in professional communications systems, but are not often encountered in amateur communications equipment. The basic function of a noise gate is to allow the signal to pass through normally if it is above a certain threshold level. If it is below that level, the signal is either switched off altogether, or attenuated by a substantial amount (usually 20dB or more). When there is a poor signal to noise ratio this cuts off the annoying background "hiss" during pauses in the voice signal. In fact a noise gate can be used to combat any type of noise, but it tends to be most effective with ordinary "hiss" type background noise. In an amateur radio context this means that it is most likely to be of benefit when DXing on the h.f. and v.h.f. bands.

Of course, a noise gate does not actually provide any increase in the signal to noise ratio of the signal. It provides a lower background noise level during pauses in the voice signal, but it does not give any improvement when the signal is switched through to the output. It is during the pauses that the noise is most noticeable and intrusive, and a noise gate can give a subjective improvement in the signal. It might not actually make the signal any more intelligible, but at the very least it will break up the monotonous background "hiss" which can soon become irksome, making it difficult to concentrate on the main signal.

A volume expander is a slightly refined version of a noise gate. The simple on/off switching of a noise gate tends to be very obvious in operation. A noise gate is rather more subtle in that it enables a high level signal to pass normally, but it will provide a varying degree of attenuation on lower level signals. The lower the signal level, the greater the attenuation. This still gives the lower noise level during pauses in the signal, but by varying the gain instead of simply switching it between two levels the action of the circuit is less readily apparent. Noise gates and expanders can both do a good job, but my preference is certainly for the volume expander.

Circuit Operation

Figure 2.27 shows the circuit diagram for a simple but effective volume expander. This is based on an NE570N or NE571N integrated circuit, and these components are specifically designed for use in volume compression and expansion applications. The only difference between these two integrated circuits is that the NE570N has slightly superior performance figures. In this non hi-fi application either device should work perfectly well, and I used an NE570N merely as I happened to have one of these in the spares box. The NE570N and NE571N are actually dual devices which contain two sets of electronic building blocks. Each set of blocks can be configured as an expander or a compressor. In this case one set of blocks is used as an expander while the other set is ignored.

IC1 acts as a buffer stage at the input of the circuit. C3 and C4 couple the output of IC1 to the gain control cell of IC2 and to its rectifier/smoothing circuit. C6 is the smoothing capacitor in the smoothing circuit. The positive d.c. output signal from the smoothing circuit is proportional to the strength of the input signal, and it is used as the control signal for the gain control block. Therefore, as the strength of the input signal rises, so does the gain of the gain control cell. This gives the desired volume expansion effect.

R3 is a bias resistor for an operational amplifier which functions as a buffer stage at the output of the circuit. A distortion trimming circuit can be connected to pin 8 of IC2, but for this application the untrimmed distortion will be quite low enough. Accordingly, decoupling capacitor C5 is connected to pin 8 in order to aid good stability, but it is otherwise left unconnected. The supply current from a 9 volt supply is about 4 to 5 milliamps.

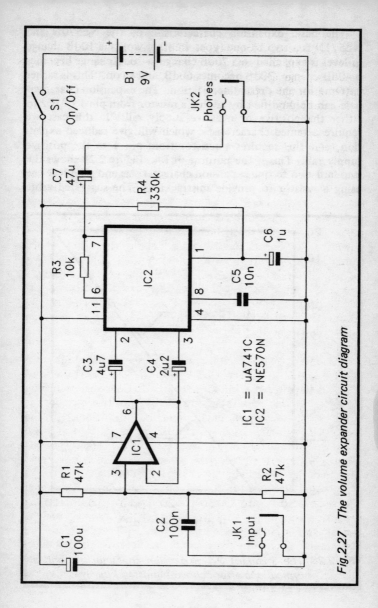

Fig.2.27 The volume expander circuit diagram

The basic expansion characteristic of the NE570N and NE571N is a two to one type. In other words, a 10dB change in level is expanded to a 20dB change, a 20dB change becomes a 40dB change, 30dB becomes 60dB, and so on. This is rather extreme for the present application. The expansion characteristic can be modified by adding a resistor from pin 1 of IC2 to either the positive or negative supply rail. In this case we require a tamed characteristic which will give reduced expansion, and this requires a resistor from pin 1 to the positive supply rail. This is the purpose of R4. Figure 2.28 shows the standard two to one expansion characteristic and a typical one using a resistor to provide mistracking. The suggested value

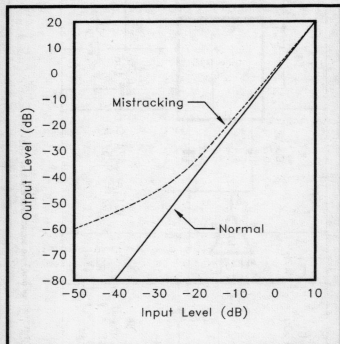

Fig.2.28 The standard 2.1 expansion characteristic and a typical one after deliberate mistracking

for R4 should give good results, but you might like to experiment with other values. A higher value gives increased expansion — a lower value gives reduced expansion.

Components for Volume Expander (Fig.2.27)

Resistors (all 0.25 watt 5% carbon film)
R1	47k
R2	47k
R3	10k
R4	330k (see text)

Capacitors
C1	100µ 10V elect
C2	100n polyester
C3	4µ7 63V elect
C4	2µ2 63V elect
C5	10n polyester
C6	1µ 63V elect
C7	47µ 63V elect

Semiconductors
IC1	µA741C
IC2	NE570N or NE571N (see text)

Miscellaneous
S1	s.p.s.t. min toggle
B1	9 volt (PP3 size)
JK1	Standard jack socket
JK2	Standard jack socket
	Case, 8 pin d.i.l. i.c. holder, 16 pin d.i.l. i.c. holder, circuit board, battery connector, wire, solder, etc.

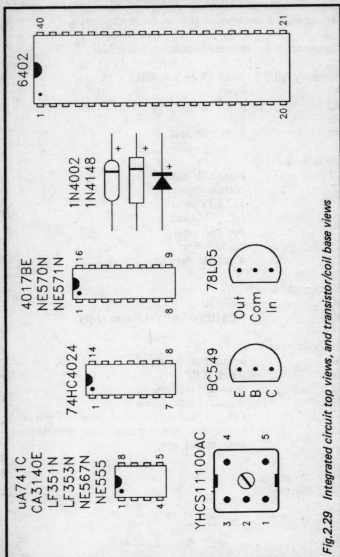

Fig.2.29   Integrated circuit top views, and transistor/coil base views